Counselors' Pages

Forms, Activity Sheets, Sample Lesson Plans, And Letters
To Help Elementary School Counselors
Spend More Time Counseling Children And Less Time On Paperwork

Written By
Rebecca C. Schmidt, M. Ed.

COUNSELORS' PAGES

10-DIGIT ISBN: 1-57543-140-8 13-DIGIT ISBN: 978-1-57543-140-6

GRAPHIC DESIGN: Cameon Funk

Published by mar*co products, inc.
1443 Old York Road
Warminster, PA 18974
1-800-448-2197
www.marcoproducts.com

PRINTED IN THE U.S.A.

Contents

Dear Fellow Counselors:

I have been counseling preschoolers through fifth-grade children for 13 years. Through the years, I have developed charts, signs, teacher letters, parent letters, and other forms regarding student activities, behavior-management plans, parent tips, teacher tips, and small-group guidance ideas. I have used these year after year so I need not "reinvent the wheel" every time a problem recurs.

Do you have trouble with students tattling incessantly?
Use the *Tattle Form* (page 47).

Do parents ask you how to handle tantrums at home?
Use the *Steps To Trample Tantrums* script (pages 50-51).

Do students complain about being bullied?
Use the *Bully Buster Box Letter* (page 94).

Are the same clique of girls often in your office with friendship issues?
Use the *Dear Friend* letter (pages 132-133).

Feel free to reproduce these forms, sign your name, and use them over and over. If you find that some of the information on the forms does not fit your particular situation, you may adapt them using the provided CD-Rom (inside back cover) containing editable Microsoft Word® files of many of the letters/forms found in this book. After adapting a Microsoft Word® document, you may give the form/letter your own personal touch by adding graphics and color, then printing it on school letterhead or color/specialty paper. Also provided are color PDF files of the posters and worksheets (these can not be edited). To use these files, you will need Microsoft Word® 2000 or newer and Adobe Reader® 5.0 or newer (compatible with Windows 2000® or newer or Mac OS 9.0® or newer). Adapting them to your own personal situation will still save you time because you will not be creating a form from scratch. (For more information regarding the included CD, see page 248.)

These forms and strategies have made my job easier. I hope they will do the same for you.

Codes in each section will help identify when to use each form. The codes are as follows:

- IND = Individual Counseling
- SG = Small-Group Counseling
- CG = Classroom Guidance
- SW = School-Wide Program
- PH = Parent Handout
- SH = Student Handout
- TH = Teacher Handout
- SA = Suggested Activities
- AH = Administrator Handout
- CR = Counselor Resources

Behavior Management

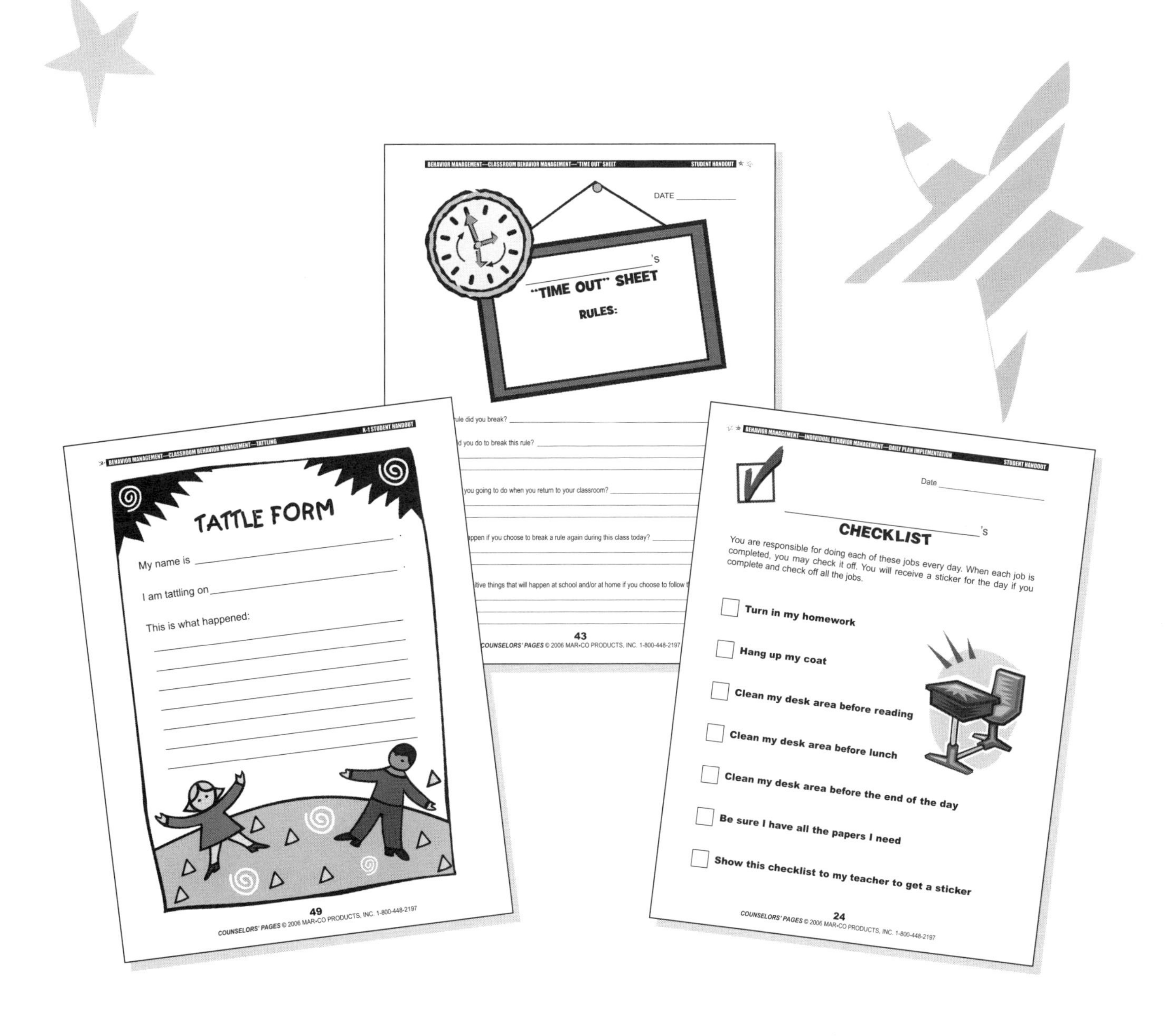

BEHAVIOR MANAGEMENT—CLASSROOM BEHAVIOR MANAGEMENT—"TIME OUT" SHEET STUDENT HANDOUT

DATE ___________

___________'s

"TIME OUT" SHEET

RULES:

...rule did you break? ___________

...d you do to break this rule? ___________

...you going to do when you return to your classroom? ___________

...appen if you choose to break a rule again during this class today? ___________

...itive things that will happen at school and/or at home if you choose to follow t...

43

COUNSELORS' PAGES © 2006 MAR•CO PRODUCTS, INC. 1-800-448-2197

BEHAVIOR MANAGEMENT—CLASSROOM BEHAVIOR MANAGEMENT—TATTLING K-1 STUDENT HANDOUT

TATTLE FORM

My name is ___________

I am tattling on ___________

This is what happened: ___________

49

COUNSELORS' PAGES © 2006 MAR•CO PRODUCTS, INC. 1-800-448-2197

BEHAVIOR MANAGEMENT—INDIVIDUAL BEHAVIOR MANAGEMENT—DAILY PLAN IMPLEMENTATION STUDENT HANDOUT

Date ___________

___________'s

CHECKLIST

You are responsible for doing each of these jobs every day. When each job is completed, you may check it off. You will receive a sticker for the day if you complete and check off all the jobs.

- [ ] Turn in my homework
- [ ] Hang up my coat
- [ ] Clean my desk area before reading
- [ ] Clean my desk area before lunch
- [ ] Clean my desk area before the end of the day
- [ ] Be sure I have all the papers I need
- [ ] Show this checklist to my teacher to get a sticker

24

COUNSELORS' PAGES © 2006 MAR•CO PRODUCTS, INC. 1-800-448-2197

INDIVIDUAL BEHAVIOR MANAGEMENT

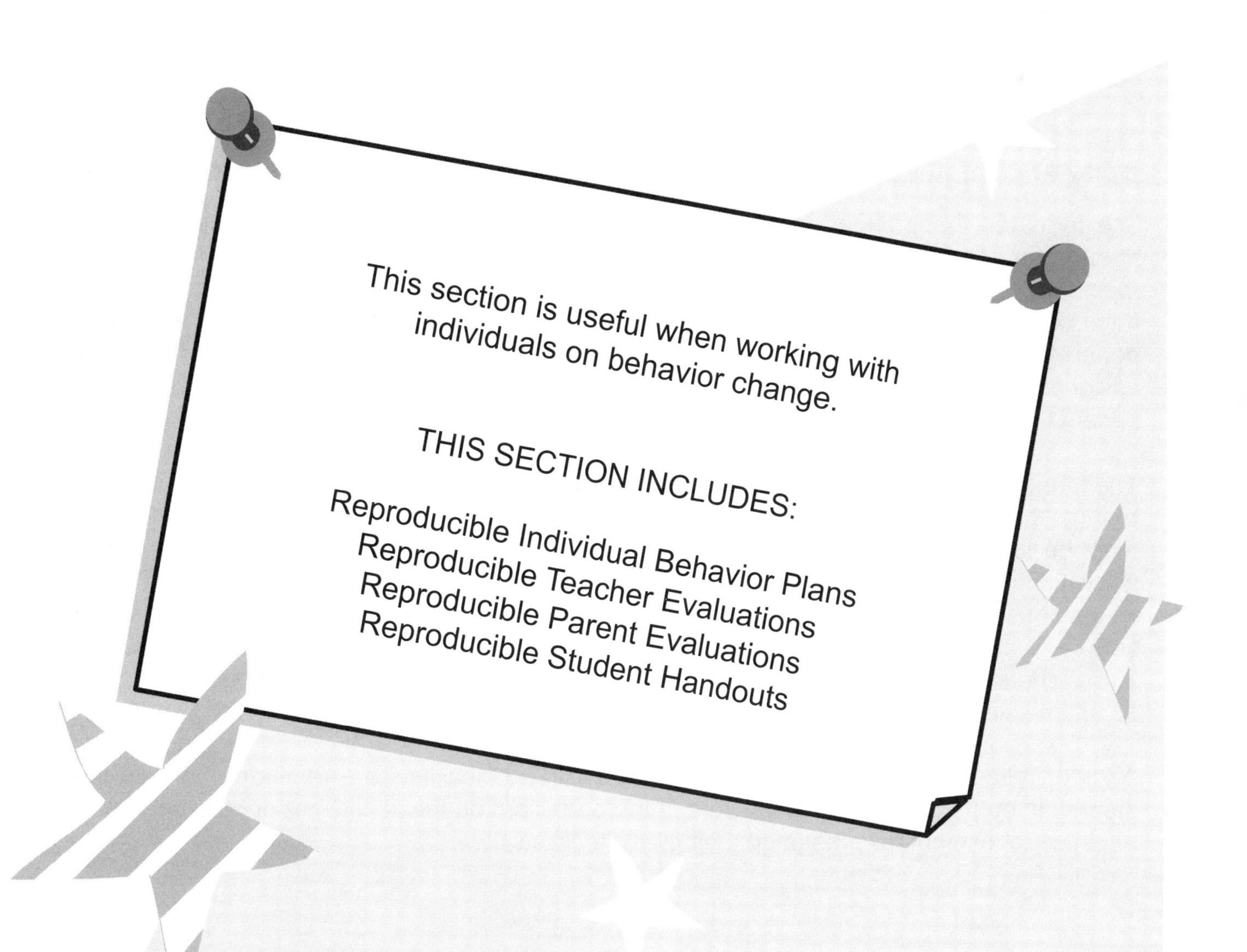

Fun Folders (pages 14-25) **IND**

A *Fun Folder* is a simple pocket folder that includes an individual behavior plan, a daily implementation plan, and a sticker calendar. A sheet of stickers is stapled to the inside of the folder. Each child chooses the color of his/her folder. The outside of the folder is decorated with colorful stickers and the title "_______________'s Fun Folder."

Individual Behavior Plans (pages 14-19) **IND SH**

The counselor first chooses an individual behavior plan that targets the behaviors the teacher or parent want the child to improve (pages 14-19). Several of the included forms can be used for this purpose. One format lists the rules. In another, the rules must be identified. One format includes the number of stickers and rewards, and one is left open-ended for the counselor to insert the number of stickers required and what the rewards will be.

Before selecting a form, discuss with the student the rules to be followed. Once the rules have been identified, select one of the forms and, if necessary, complete it. The completed form should be placed in the student's *Fun Folder* and will identify the rules to be followed and the number of stickers required to receive a reward. This is the first part of the student's individual behavior plan.

Daily Plan Implementation (pages 20-25) **IND SH**

The forms on these pages show how the selected individual behavior plan will be implemented on a daily basis. There are several forms from which to choose. The first choice (pages 20-21) asks the student to monitor his/her behavior throughout the day by keeping track of the number of times an action was required and the number of times the student performed that action. For example, a student may write that he/she completed 4 out of 6 assignments on a particular day. The form on page 20 lists specific behaviors. The one on page 21 has been left blank for the counselor to fill in the appropriate behaviors.

The forms on pages 22-23 ask the student to keep track of behaviors for particular time slots. Using either the form in which actions are identified (page 22) or the one on which the actions must be filled in (page 23), divide the day into three time slots according to your school's particular time schedule. The first slot would be for time between arriving at school and when instructional time begins (e.g., 8:00-9:00). The second slot would be for morning instructional time (e.g., 9:00-11:30). The last slot would be for afternoon instructional time (e.g., 12:25-2:45). The student then writes down the number of times he/she performed each action in each time slot during the day.

Another type of form is the checklist (pages 24-25). Checklists are reminders to help the student keep track of his/her behaviors. If the behaviors on these lists are not the behaviors desired, counselors may make up their own checklists.

Teacher And Parent Evaluations (pages 26-28) **TH PH**

These forms are for the teacher (pages 26-27) and for the teacher and parent (page 28) to complete. They should be returned to the counselor on a specific date and include the number of times the action was performed in each time slot.

Sticker Calendars For Behavior Plans (pages 29-31) **IND SH**

Choose a calendar to accompany the behavior plan chosen. Using the selected evaluation form, record the number of stickers earned daily. When a student accumulates enough stickers to earn a reward, give the student the reward or allow him/her to accumulate more stickers for a greater reward. An adult should affix the stickers to the calendar.

Bus Behavior Plan (page 32) **IND SH**

Reproduce this form for students who need to improve their behavior on the bus.

______________________________'s

FUN FOLDER

I will choose to follow these rules:

1. ______________________________

2. ______________________________

Each time I follow these rules, I will get a sticker.

1 sticker	=	**A surprise from the counselor.** (I get to call the counselor, be invited to his/her office, and receive an award. The phone number at school is ______________________.)
2 stickers	=	**Choose what the family has for dinner.** (Choose something from each of the five food groups.)
4 stickers	=	**Play a game with the family for 20 minutes.**
6 stickers	=	**Choose a video to watch or choose two board games to play.**
8 stickers	=	**Paint pictures with Mom or Dad.**
10 stickers	=	**Go to get a special treat.**
13 stickers	=	**Go to the playground.**
16 stickers	=	**Choose two items at the Dollar Store.** (You have 10 minutes to make your choice.)
20 stickers	=	**Choose a parent-approved video to rent**.
24 stickers	=	**Be the "parent" for 15 minutes and have Mom and Dad be the children.** (Set a timer so you will know when the time is up.)
30 stickers	=	**Choose your own parent-approved reward**.
40 stickers	=	**Choose a parent-approved movie to see at the theater and invite a friend to join you.**

______________________'s

FUN FOLDER

I will choose to follow these rules:

1. ______________________

2. ______________________

When I choose to follow these rules, I will get a sticker. Stickers add up to grown-up privileges, fun activities, and even prizes!

2 stickers = **A surprise from the counselor.**
(I get to call the counselor, be invited to his/her office, and receive an award. The phone number at school is ______________________.)

4 stickers = **Choose what the family has for dinner.**
(Be sure to choose from the five food groups.)

8 stickers = **Play a game with the family for 20 minutes.**

12 stickers = **Help make dinner.**

16 stickers = **Choose a special TV show for the whole family to watch.**

20 stickers = **Choose a song for the family to dance to.**

26 stickers = **Sleep in a sleeping bag anywhere in the house you want, except Mom and Dad's room, for one night.**

34 stickers = **Choose three items at the Dollar Store.**
(You have 20 minutes to make your choice.)

42 stickers = **Choose a special reward or privilege.**
(Make sure Mom and Dad say it is okay.)

54 stickers = **Be the "parent" for 15 minutes and have Mom and Dad be the children.**
(Set a timer so you will know when the time is up.)

68 stickers = **Go to a store and choose something for $5.00.**

80 stickers = **Choose a parent-approved movie to see at the theater and invite a friend to join you.**

If I choose not to follow these rules, I will have the following consequences:

____

____

_______________________________'s

FUN FOLDER

I will choose to follow these rules:

1. I will follow directions the first time asked.
2. I will do my work as quickly as possible and do it to the best of my ability.

When I choose to follow these rules, I will get one sticker for following directions and one for completing my work. I can earn two stickers every day.

2 stickers = **A surprise from the counselor.**
(I get to call the counselor, be invited to his/her office, and receive an award. The phone number at school is _______________________________.)

4 stickers = **Choose what the family has for dinner.**
(Something from each of the five food groups.)

8 stickers = **Play a game with the family for 20 minutes.**

12 stickers = **Choose a song for the family to dance to.**

16 stickers = **Choose a 30-minute television show for the whole family to watch.**

20 stickers = **Choose two items at the Dollar Store.**
(You have 20 minutes to make your choice.)

26 stickers = **Sleep in a sleeping bag anywhere in the house you want, except Mom and Dad's room, for one night.**

32 stickers = **Choose three items at the Dollar Store.**
(You have 15 minutes to make your choice.)

40 stickers = **Choose a parent-approved video to rent.**

48 stickers = **Be the "parent" for 15 minutes and have Mom and Dad be the children.**
(Set a timer so you will know when the time is up.)

60 stickers = **Choose your own parent-approved reward.**

80 stickers = **Choose a parent-approved movie to see at the theater and invite a friend to join you.**

______________________________'s

RESPONSIBILITY FOLDER

I will follow these rules:

1. I will think before I say something or do something.
2. I will be honest if I say or do something inappropriate.
3. I will not make excuses for my behavior.

When I choose to follow these rules, I will get a sticker. Stickers add up to fun privileges, fun activities, and even prizes!

2 stickers = A surprise from the counselor.
(I get to call the counselor, be invited to his/her office, and receive an award. The phone number at school is ______________________________.)

4 stickers = Have 30 minutes of computer time with a friend in my classroom.

8 stickers = Play a game with the family for 20 minutes.

12 stickers = Eat in the living room.

16 stickers = Choose a 30-minute television show for the whole family to watch.

20 stickers = Choose a song for the family to dance to.

26 stickers = Sleep in a sleeping bag anywhere in the house you want, except Mom and Dad's room, for one night.

32 stickers = Have a special lunch with my teacher.

40 stickers = Choose a parent-approved reward at home or a teacher-approved reward at school.

48 stickers = Be the "parent" for 15 minutes and have Mom and Dad be the children.
(Set a timer so you will know when the time is up.)

60 stickers = Go to the store and choose something costing no more than $5.00.

80 stickers = Choose a parent-approved movie to see at the theater and invite a friend to join you.

If I choose not to follow these rules, I will have the following consequences:

____

____

______________________________'s

FUN FOLDER

I will choose to follow these rules:

1. I will listen and not talk when others are talking.
2. I will follow directions and do my work carefully.

When I choose to follow these rules, I will get a sticker. Stickers add up to fun privileges, fun activities, and even prizes!

2 stickers	**=**	**A surprise from the counselor.** (I get to call the counselor, be invited to his/her office, and receive an award. The phone number at school is ______________________________.)
4 stickers	**=**	**Have 30 minutes of computer time with a friend in my classroom.**
8 stickers	**=**	**Play a game with the family for 20 minutes.**
12 stickers	**=**	**Eat in the living room.**
16 stickers	**=**	**Choose a 30-minute television show for the whole family to watch.**
20 stickers	**=**	**Choose a song for the family to dance to.**
26 stickers	**=**	**Sleep in a sleeping bag anywhere in the house you want, except Mom and Dad's room, for one night.**
32 stickers	**=**	**Have a special lunch with my teacher.**
40 stickers	**=**	**Choose a parent-approved reward at home or a teacher-approved reward at school.**
48 stickers	**=**	**Be the "parent" for 15 minutes and have Mom and Dad be the children.** (Set a timer so you will know when the time is up.)
60 stickers	**=**	**Go to the store and choose something costing no more than $5.00.**
80 stickers	**=**	**Choose a parent-approved movie to see at the theater and invite a friend to join you.**

If I choose not to follow these rules, I will have the following consequences:

____

____

______________________________'s

FUN FOLDER

I will choose to follow these rules:

1. ______________________________

2. ______________________________

When I choose to follow these rules, I will get a sticker. Stickers add up to prizes and fun activities. The rewards I can earn are:

____ **stickers** = ______________________________

____ **stickers** = ______________________________

____ **stickers** = ______________________________

____ **stickers** = ______________________________

____ **stickers** = ______________________________

____ **stickers** = ______________________________

____ **stickers** = ______________________________

____ **stickers** = ______________________________

____ **stickers** = ______________________________

____ **stickers** = ______________________________

____ **stickers** = ______________________________

____ **stickers** = ______________________________

____ **stickers** = ______________________________

____ **stickers** = ______________________________

____ **stickers** = ______________________________

____ **stickers** = ______________________________

____ **stickers** = ______________________________

____ **stickers** = ______________________________

DAILY PLAN SCHEDULE

Directions: Look at the list of behaviors below. On a separate sheet of paper, keep track of the number of times you were required to perform each action each day. On the same sheet of paper, keep track of the number of times you actually performed the action. Under the appropriate day of the week, record the number of times you performed the action in the box above the words "out of" and the number of times you could have performed the action in the box above the word "times."

NAME ____

WEEK OF ____

	MON.	TUES.	WED.	THURS.	FRI.
I completed my schoolwork.	☐ OUT OF ☐ TIMES	☐ OUT OF ☐ TIMES	☐ OUT OF ☐ TIMES	☐ OUT OF ☐ TIMES	☐ OUT OF ☐ TIMES
I completed my homework.	☐ OUT OF ☐ TIMES	☐ OUT OF ☐ TIMES	☐ OUT OF ☐ TIMES	☐ OUT OF ☐ TIMES	☐ OUT OF ☐ TIMES
I followed directions the first time they were given.	☐ OUT OF ☐ TIMES	☐ OUT OF ☐ TIMES	☐ OUT OF ☐ TIMES	☐ OUT OF ☐ TIMES	☐ OUT OF ☐ TIMES
I kept my hands and feet to myself.	☐ OUT OF ☐ TIMES	☐ OUT OF ☐ TIMES	☐ OUT OF ☐ TIMES	☐ OUT OF ☐ TIMES	☐ OUT OF ☐ TIMES

DAILY PLAN SCHEDULE

Directions: Look at the list of behaviors below. On a separate sheet of paper, keep track of the number of times you were required to perform each action each day. On the same sheet of paper, keep track of the number of times you actually performed the action. Under the appropriate day of the week, record the number of times you performed the action in the box above the words "out of" and the number of times you could have performed the action in the box above the word "times."

NAME ______________________________

WEEK OF ______________________________

	MON.	TUES.	WED.	THURS.	FRI.
	OUT OF TIMES	OUT OF TIMES	OUT OF TIMES	OUT OF TIMES	OUT OF TIMES
	OUT OF TIMES	OUT OF TIMES	OUT OF TIMES	OUT OF TIMES	OUT OF TIMES
	OUT OF TIMES	OUT OF TIMES	OUT OF TIMES	OUT OF TIMES	OUT OF TIMES
	OUT OF TIMES	OUT OF TIMES	OUT OF TIMES	OUT OF TIMES	OUT OF TIMES

DAILY PLAN RECORD

Directions: The behaviors you are trying to improve are listed below. A time period is written on each line. Record the number of times you performed each action in each time period during the day. Record it on the line on which the time period is written.

NAME ______________________________

WEEK OF ______________________________

	TIME PERIOD	MON.	TUES.	WED.	THURS.	FRI.
I stayed in my assigned area.						
When an adult was talking, I raised my hand.						
I looked people in the eyes when they were talking.						
I tried to solve problems by myself by trying two things before asking for help.						

DAILY PLAN RECORD

Directions: The behaviors you are trying to improve are listed below. A time period is written on each line. Record the number of times you performed each action in each time period during the day. Record it on the line on which the time period is written.

NAME ____

WEEK OF ____

	TIME PERIOD	MON.	TUES.	WED.	THURS.	FRI.

Date ____________________

____________________________________'s

CHECKLIST

You are responsible for doing each of these jobs every day. When each job is completed, you may check it off. You will receive a sticker for the day if you complete and check off all the jobs.

- ☐ **Turn in my homework**
- ☐ **Hang up my coat**
- ☐ **Clean my desk area before reading**
- ☐ **Clean my desk area before lunch**
- ☐ **Clean my desk area before the end of the day**
- ☐ **Be sure I have all the papers I need**
- ☐ **Show this checklist to my teacher to get a sticker**

Date ______________________

__________________________________'s

GOOD-BEHAVIOR CHECKLIST

1. I participated in all classroom activities.

☐ **YES** ☐ **NO**

2. I stayed with the group and did not wander around the room.

☐ **YES** ☐ **NO**

3. I began and finished my work on time.

☐ **YES** ☐ **NO**

4. I cleaned up my table/desk and did not leave a mess.

☐ **YES** ☐ **NO**

5. I listened and did not talk back to any adult.

☐ **YES** ☐ **NO**

6. I did not get upset and pout when things did not go my way.

☐ **YES** ☐ **NO**

TEACHER EVALUATION

NAME ______________________________ DATE ___________

I need help monitoring this child's behavior. If the child followed the rule during that time period, please put a checkmark in the box. If the child did not follow the rule, write a minus sign in the box. Then return the completed sheet to me on_______________________ . Thank you for your cooperation.

	BEFORE SCHOOL	MORNING	LUNCH RECESS	AFTERNOON
Follows directions the first time				
Keeps hands and feet to self				
Lets others do their work				
Takes responsibility for behavior				

TEACHER EVALUATION

NAME ______________________________ DATE ___________

I need help monitoring this child's behavior. If the child followed the rule during that time period, please put a checkmark in the box. If the child did not follow the rule, write a minus sign in the box. Then return the completed sheet to me on______________________ . Thank you for your cooperation.

	BEFORE SCHOOL	MORNING	LUNCH RECESS	AFTERNOON

TEACHER AND PARENT EVALUATION

NAME ________________________________

RULE(S) ____

____

Directions: You will receive a sticker each time you follow the specified rule or rules. Take your paper home each day after your teacher has completed it and give it to your parents. Bring your paper back to school each day after your parent has completed it. Only your parents will complete your paper on Saturday and Sunday.

		BEFORE LUNCH	AFTER LUNCH	EVENING
WEEK OF	MONDAY			
	TUESDAY			
	WEDNESDAY			
	THURSDAY			
	FRIDAY			
	SATURDAY			
	SUNDAY			
WEEK OF	MONDAY			
	TUESDAY			
	WEDNESDAY			
	THURSDAY			
	FRIDAY			
	SATURDAY			
	SUNDAY			

		BEFORE LUNCH	AFTER LUNCH	EVENING
WEEK OF	MONDAY			
	TUESDAY			
	WEDNESDAY			
	THURSDAY			
	FRIDAY			
	SATURDAY			
	SUNDAY			
WEEK OF	MONDAY			
	TUESDAY			
	WEDNESDAY			
	THURSDAY			
	FRIDAY			
	SATURDAY			
	SUNDAY			

______________________'s

STICKER CALENDAR

Directions: Each day you follow the expected rule or rules, you will receive a sticker in the *School* column. If you do not follow the expected rule or rules, you will not receive a sticker in the *School* column and the rule or rules that were not followed will be written in the "Rule That Was Difficult To Follow" column.

DATE	SCHOOL	RULE THAT WAS DIFFICULT TO FOLLOW	TEACHER'S INITIALS/COMMENTS

______________________________'s

STICKER CALENDAR

Directions: The rules you are expected to follow are to be followed both at school and at home. Your calendar will be sent home each day so your parents can see how you are doing in school and add a sticker to your calendar if you follow the expected rule or rules at home. You should follow the rules on Saturday and Sunday, too.

DAY	SCHOOL	HOME	RULE THAT WAS DIFFICULT TO FOLLOW	COMMENTS
MON.				
TUES.				
WED.				
THURS.				
FRI.				
SAT.				
SUN.				

______________________________'s

STICKER CALENDAR

Directions: You will receive a sticker each time you follow the specified rule or rules. Take your paper home each day after your teacher has completed it and give it to your parents. Bring your paper back to school each day after your parent has completed it. Only your parents will complete your paper on Saturday and Sunday.

DAY	BEFORE LUNCH	AFTER LUNCH	EVENING AT HOME
MON.			
TUES.			
WED.			
THURS.			
FRI.			
SAT.			
SUN.			

BUS BEHAVIOR PLAN

Misbehavior on the school bus is a common problem. Bus drivers are responsible for the students' safety, and misbehavior endangers lives. With this plan, the bus driver completes the behavior slip by checking the appropriate answer each day and the student delivers the slip to the classroom teacher for rewards or consequences. Reproduce the forms below, cut them apart, and distribute them to the children to give to the bus driver.

BUS BEHAVIOR

Name ______________________________

Date ____________ Bus Driver's Initials _______

Today, I followed directions, stayed in my seat, and kept my hands and feet to myself!

☐ YES ☐ NO

Today, I needed two warnings to follow directions, stay in my seat, and keep my hands and feet to myself.

☐ YES ☐ NO

Today, I had to have more than two warnings and still I did not follow directions. I did not stay in my seat and I did not keep my hands and feet to myself.

☐ YES ☐ NO

BUS BEHAVIOR

Name ______________________________

Date ____________ Bus Driver's Initials _______

Today, I followed directions, stayed in my seat, and kept my hands and feet to myself!

☐ YES ☐ NO

Today, I needed two warnings to follow directions, stay in my seat, and keep my hands and feet to myself.

☐ YES ☐ NO

Today, I had to have more than two warnings and still I did not follow directions. I did not stay in my seat and I did not keep my hands and feet to myself.

☐ YES ☐ NO

Classroom Behavior Management

This section is useful when a teacher is having a difficult time with classroom discipline. It can be used with as many students in the classroom as the teacher deems necessary.

THIS SECTION INCLUDES:

Reproducible Behavior Checklists
Reproducible Parent Handouts
Reproducible Teacher Handouts
Reproducible Student Handouts

Parent Letters (pages 36-37) **IND PH**

Since a weekly evaluation sheet is to be sent home to parents, a letter (page 36) should be sent home explaining the plan before you implement it. When the student's goals have been met, another letter (page 37) should be sent home to advise parents of their child's success.

Classroom Behavior Checklists (pages 38-41) **IND TH SH**

Three of these checklists (pages 38-40) target behavior management and the fourth (page 41) focuses on work completion. These easy-to-use forms keep a running tab on the student's progress. These checklists can be modified to correspond with Individual Education Plans (IEP) and used to help the teacher and counselor document the child's progress and when IEP goals are met. Notification should be sent home to advise parents of their child's success.

"Time Out" Sheets (pages 42-43) **IND SH**

These sheets are to be completed by students who are sent to a "time-out" area, a "Reflection Room," or who must serve in-school suspension.

Teacher/Counselor Communication (pages 44-46) **IND TH**

One of the most important aspects of school counseling is teacher-counselor communication. Having these communication forms readily available will make this task easier and help the teacher keep the counselor informed about the child's progress. The forms can be adapted to reflect the goals the student and the counselor are working toward each week.

Tattling (pages 47-49) **IND SG CG SH**

These forms are to be made available for the classroom teacher and used in the classroom. They are designed to keep students from tattling. When a student tattles, the teacher simply gives the student the *Tattling Form* and says, "You know what to do." The student is responsible for filling out each detail of the incident and returning the form to the teacher. The teacher can read and investigate the incident at a later time. Students should complete the forms during recess or other free time and not during class. The form is not to be used as a punishment for tattling, but as a deterrent.

Tantrums (pages 50-51) **IND PH**

Reproduce this script for use when meeting with parents whose children have tantrums at home.

Fun Jar Positive Reinforcement Ideas (page 52) **IND PH**

This alternative to a sticker chart is to be used at home. Each reward should be cut out, folded, and placed in a decorative *Fun Jar.* The child chooses a piece of paper on which a reward is written when he/she reaches a goal.

No Fun Jar Consequence Ideas (page 53) **IND PH**

Each consequence is to be cut out, folded, and placed in a *No Fun Jar* at home. The child who breaks a rule or does not meet his/her behavior goals for the day chooses a piece of paper on which a consequence is written.

Worrying (page 54) **IND SH**

This form, to be used with a student who worries a lot, is designed to encourage the child to talk about and write about his/her worries. Once the worries are "out of his/her head" and placed "into a box," the student can forget about the worry temporarily or permanently. The counselor can use this form in the counseling office and provide a *Worry Box* to hold the worries until the student wants to discuss them again. This form can also be used at home.

Date ________________

Dear ____________________________:

Your child's teacher and I have been working on positive behaviors with the class this year. These behaviors include: following directions, remaining seated, finishing quality work, being honest, taking responsibility for actions, etc. The children have received rewards from the teacher and earned a class reward from me as well. The class chose to have an extra recess and to play kickball. When they receive 50 points, they will have a big pizza party for lunch!

Even with this positive behavior-management program, some students still do not follow the classroom rules.

Once a week, the teacher and I will send home a social/behavioral progress report for parents to discuss with their children. Please discuss the behaviors listed on the report with your child and explain how important these behaviors are to learning and making friends. A sample of the report is:

Name ____

Week of ______________________________________

1. I was a good listener and did not talk to others when the teacher was talking.
2. I followed directions.
3. I was kind to my classmates.
4. I was respectful to the teacher.
5. I took responsibility for my own actions and did not blame others for what I had done.
6. I was honest when I was asked a question about my behavior.

We have seen improvement in students' behavior and social skills since the beginning of the school year. We want to make sure that the progress continues and that every student benefits as much as he/she can from the program.

If you have any questions, please feel free to contact me. Thank you for your support.

Sincerely,

Dear ___________________________________:

Everyone in ___________________________________'s class is excited! We have been listening, following directions, and following the classroom rules. We earned 50 points for good behavior!

Earning 50 points means that we get to have a special pizza lunch in the classroom on ___________________________________. Each of us needs to bring a dollar to school that day. We may also bring any snack or dessert we would like to share with the class.

We know you are just as excited as we are. Our teacher and counselor are proud of all of us, but more importantly, we are very proud of ourselves!

Dear ___________________________________:

Everyone in ___________________________________'s class is excited! We have been listening, following directions, and following the classroom rules. We earned 50 points for good behavior!

Earning 50 points means that we get to have a special pizza lunch in the classroom on ___________________________________. Each of us needs to bring a dollar to school that day. We may also bring any snack or dessert we would like to share with the class.

We know you are just as excited as we are. Our teacher and counselor are proud of all of us, but more importantly, we are very proud of ourselves!

______________________________'s

CHECKLIST

DATE ____/____/_______ MINUTES IN SESSION OR MINUTES OF OBSERVATION_____

GOAL	SKILL TAUGHT	SKILL EXHIBITED/LOCATION
Chooses a friend or group to play with		
Gets children's attention by speaking politely and appropriately		
Takes turns and shares		
Plays cooperatively with a friend or group		
Lets others take turns choosing activities		
Walks away from friends who are breaking rules		

Date ________________

Today _________________________ and I worked on the skill(s) checked below:

- ☐ Chooses a friend or group to play with
- ☐ Gets children's attention by speaking politely and appropriately
- ☐ Plays cooperatively with a friend or group
- ☐ Takes turns and shares
- ☐ Lets others take turns choosing activities
- ☐ Walks away from friends who are breaking rules

Date ________________

Today _________________________ and I worked on the skill(s) checked below:

- ☐ Chooses a friend or group to play with
- ☐ Gets children's attention by speaking politely and appropriately
- ☐ Plays cooperatively with a friend or group
- ☐ Takes turns and shares
- ☐ Lets others take turns choosing activities
- ☐ Walks away from friends who are breaking rules

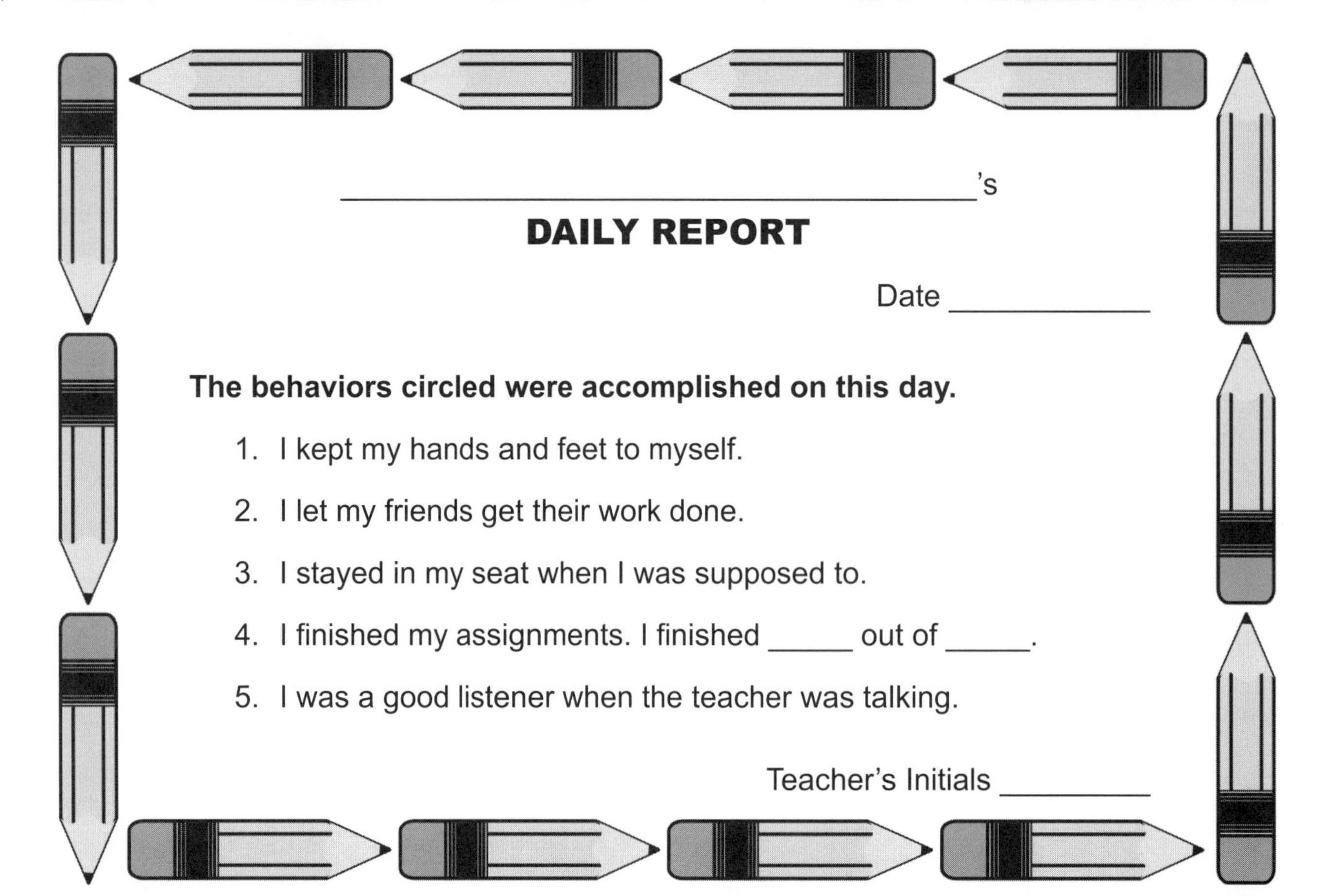

______________________________'s

DAILY REPORT

Date ___________

The behaviors circled were accomplished on this day.

1. I kept my hands and feet to myself.
2. I let my friends get their work done.
3. I stayed in my seat when I was supposed to.
4. I finished my assignments. I finished _____ out of _____.
5. I was a good listener when the teacher was talking.

Teacher's Initials _________

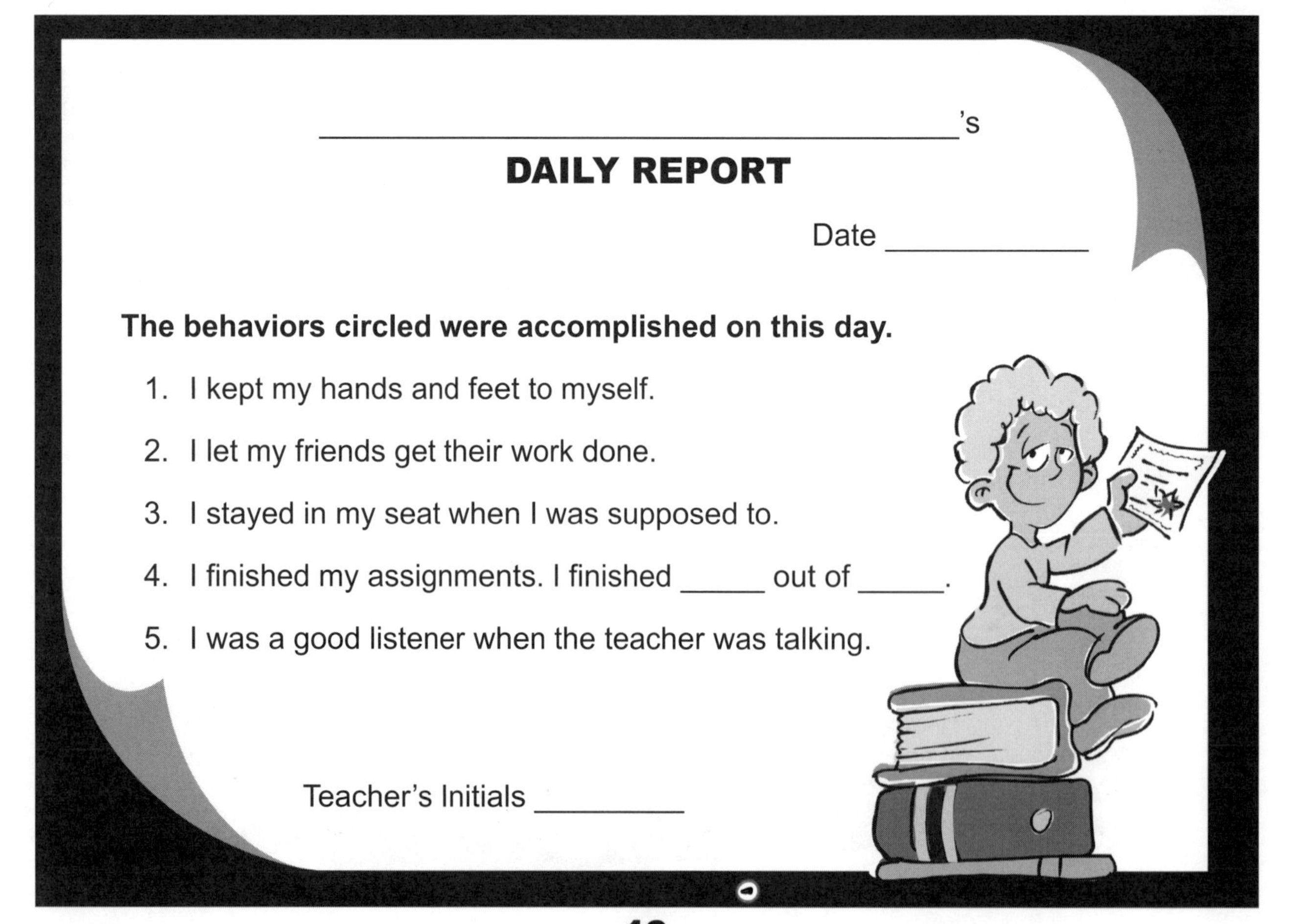

______________________________'s

DAILY REPORT

Date ___________

The behaviors circled were accomplished on this day.

1. I kept my hands and feet to myself.
2. I let my friends get their work done.
3. I stayed in my seat when I was supposed to.
4. I finished my assignments. I finished _____ out of _____.
5. I was a good listener when the teacher was talking.

Teacher's Initials _________

WORK COMPLETION BI-WEEKLY REPORT

NAME ______________________________

A checkmark (✔) in the box shows I controlled my behavior.
The second column is a record of my completed work.

WEEK OF [ ]

	I WAS IN CONTROL	I COMPLETED MY ASSIGNMENTS
MONDAY	☐	I COMPLETED _____ OF _____
TUESDAY	☐	I COMPLETED _____ OF _____
WEDNESDAY	☐	I COMPLETED _____ OF _____
THURSDAY	☐	I COMPLETED _____ OF _____
FRIDAY	☐	I COMPLETED _____ OF _____

WEEK OF [ ]

	I WAS IN CONTROL	I COMPLETED MY ASSIGNMENTS
MONDAY	☐	I COMPLETED _____ OF _____
TUESDAY	☐	I COMPLETED _____ OF _____
WEDNESDAY	☐	I COMPLETED _____ OF _____
THURSDAY	☐	I COMPLETED _____ OF _____
FRIDAY	☐	I COMPLETED _____ OF _____

DATE _______________

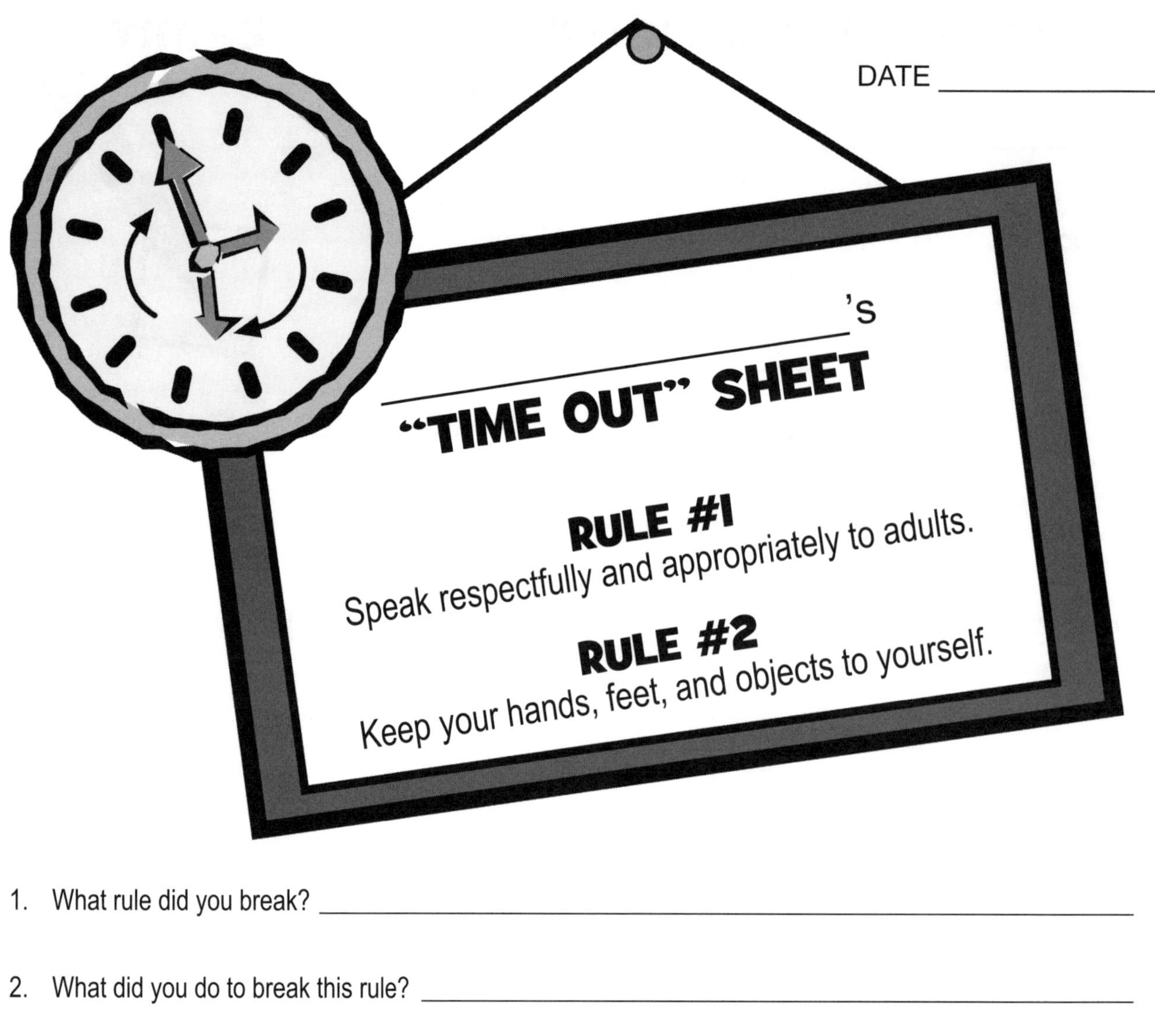

1. What rule did you break? ______________________________

2. What did you do to break this rule? ______________________________

3. What are you going to do when you return to your classroom? ______________________________

4. What will happen if you choose to break a rule again during this class today? ______________________________

5. Write two positive things that will happen at school and/or at home if you choose to follow the rules above.

DATE ______________

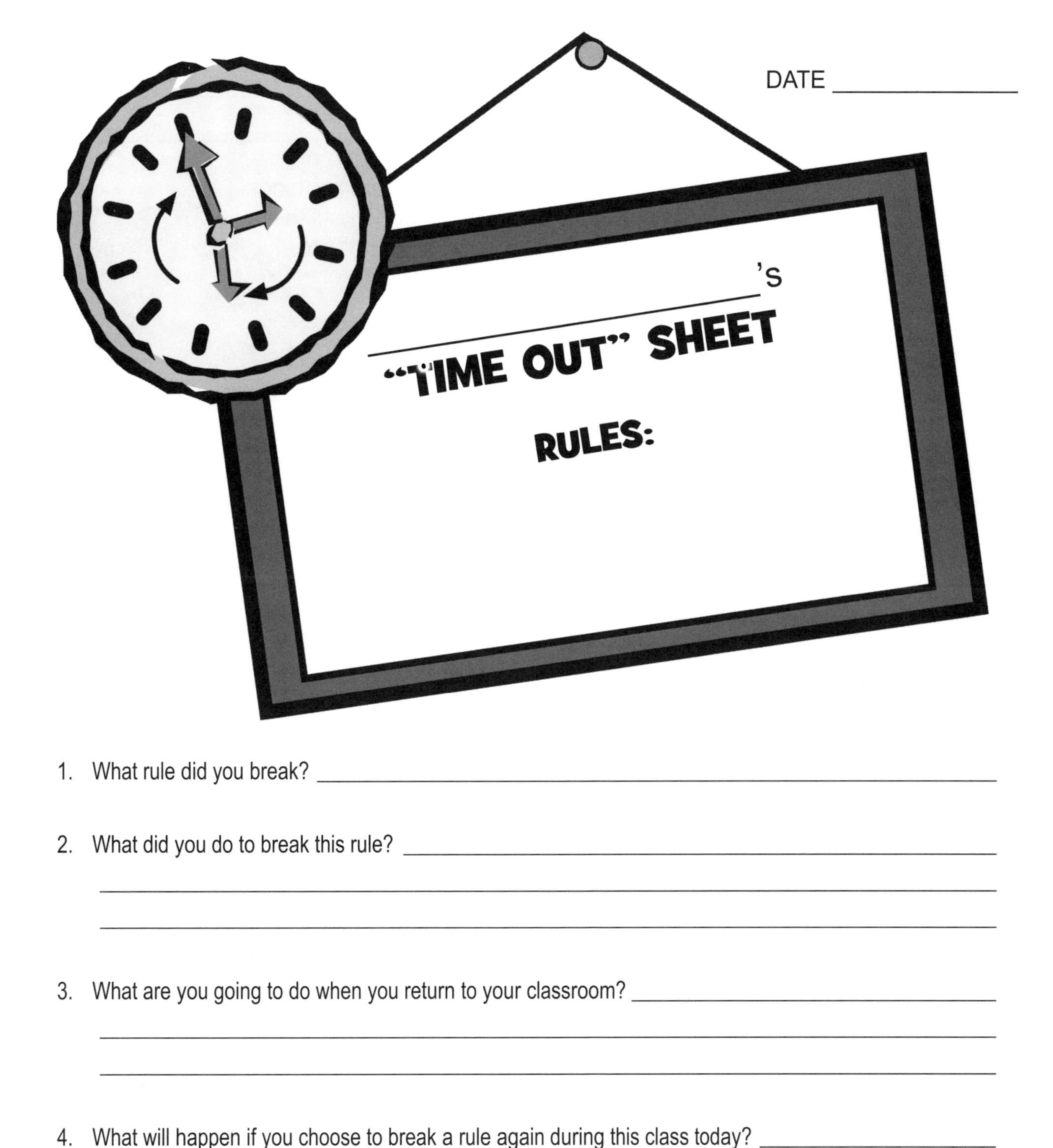

1. What rule did you break? ____________________

2. What did you do to break this rule? ____________________

3. What are you going to do when you return to your classroom? ____________________

4. What will happen if you choose to break a rule again during this class today? ____________________

5. Write two positive things that will happen at school and/or at home if you choose to follow the rules above.

WEEKLY REPORT

STUDENT'S NAME ________________ **WEEK OF** ________________

Please write some things this student did well this week and some things he/she may need to improve. Please include examples. I will contact the parents on the last school day this week. Please place one of these completed forms in my box before the morning of the last school day of this week.

Thank you,

____
COUNSELOR

MONDAY

TUESDAY

WEDNESDAY

THURSDAY

FRIDAY

UPDATE

DATE ______

Please let me know how ______________________________ is doing.

Please check one the following:

1. **How is his/her behavior?**

☐ BETTER ☐ THE SAME ☐ WORSE (Please explain briefly.)

2. **How has he/she acted with friends?**

☐ BETTER ☐ THE SAME ☐ WORSE (Please explain briefly.)

Teacher's Signature ______________________________ *Thank you.*

UPDATE

DATE ______

Please let me know how ______________________________ is doing.

Please check one the following:

1. **How is his/her behavior?**

☐ BETTER ☐ THE SAME ☐ WORSE (Please explain briefly.)

2. **How has he/she acted with friends?**

☐ BETTER ☐ THE SAME ☐ WORSE (Please explain briefly.)

Teacher's Signature ______________________________ *Thank you.*

Dear Teacher,

______________________________ is working on listening and following directions in our group. Please check the box that describes his/her behavior last week.

☐ **LISTENED MUCH BETTER** ☐ **LISTENED THE SAME AS ALWAYS**

☐ **HAD LOTS OF TROUBLE LISTENING** ☐ **NEVER A PROBLEM**

Please return this evaluation sheet to my box before _______________ .

Thank you,

- -

Dear Teacher,

______________________________ is working on listening and following directions in our group. Please check the box that describes his/her behavior last week.

☐ **LISTENED MUCH BETTER** ☐ **LISTENED THE SAME AS ALWAYS**

☐ **HAD LOTS OF TROUBLE LISTENING** ☐ **NEVER A PROBLEM**

Please return this evaluation sheet to my box before _______________ .

Thank you,

Tattle Form

STUDENT'S NAME ____________________ DATE OF PROBLEM ____________

Complete all of the questions using correct punctuation, capitalization, and complete sentences.

1. Where and at what time did this happen?

____

2. Write exactly what happened.

____

____

____

3. What are the names of everyone involved in this situation?

____

4. Where and who was the closest adult?

____

5. Describe where the other boys and girls were.

____

6. What is the name of the person you are telling on?

____

7. Did this person physically hurt someone, hurt someone's feelings, or keep someone from learning? How did he/she do that?

____

____

____

over➡

8. How could you help this person so something like this doesn't happen again?

____

____

9. What could you do to be this person's friend?

____

____

____

10. What advice would you give this person?

____

____

11. How do you think an adult should handle this situation?

____

____

12. Have you ever behaved like this towards someone before? __________
If yes, write about it. If no, write about why you haven't.

____

____

____

13. What five important things should you do to be a great friend?

____

____

____

____

____

TATTLE FORM

My name is ____ .

I am tattling on______________________________________ .

This is what happened:

____

____

____

____

____

____

STEPS TO TRAMPLE TANTRUMS

1. Calmly discuss this plan with your child when you are both calm. Do not discuss this during or right after your child has had a tantrum.

2. Say to your child, ***"There are lots of things that make people angry. It's perfectly okay to be angry. It is not okay to be out of control when you are angry."***

3. Say, ***"There are three anger rules that need to be followed:***

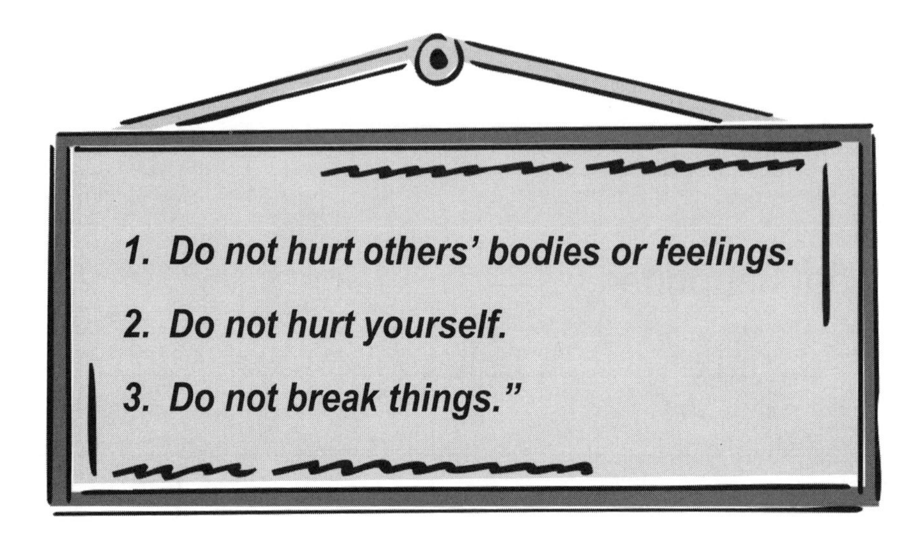

Write these rules on a poster and hang the poster in your house. Practice the rules by giving your child examples and letting him/her guess which rule was broken in each example.

4. Say, ***"There are lots of things you can do when you are angry without breaking the anger rules. You can punch a pillow, scream into a pillow or into the crook of your elbow, rip up a tissue, scribble on paper, or pound clay."*** Practice these ways of expressing your anger.

5. Say, ***"From now on, you will be expected to handle your anger like a (CHILD'S AGE)-year-old, and not a two- or three-year-old. You know how to use your words."***

6. Say, ***"When you get angry, you need to go to a quiet place or to the Anger Center*** (a place you and your child can create with all of the tools listed in Step 4) ***to calm down and get rid of your angry energy. You will be expected to follow the anger rules in the Anger Center and everywhere else. Mom and Dad and everyone in the house will use the Anger Center, too."***

over ➡

7. Say, ***"If you choose to act like a (CHILD'S AGE)-year-old and control your anger, you will be allowed to choose from the Fun Jar.*** (This is a list of fun activities and privileges that are written on strips of paper and placed in a jar. Or your child may get a sticker for a chart or whatever reward your child and you choose.)

8. Say, ***"If you choose to yell and scream, hit, kick, or say hurtful things to others, I will time you to see how long you chose to lose control."*** (Do not react to the tantrum. Simply look at your watch. If the audience is removed, the child will probably stop the "performance.")

9. Say, ***"If you choose to be out of control for 15 minutes, you will go to bed 15 minutes earlier that evening. If you choose to be out of control for three hours, you will go to bed three hours earlier than you usually do. It is completely YOUR CHOICE. If you are so out of control that you are choosing to act like a three-year-old and throwing a tantrum, you are choosing to be treated like a three-year-old and you will have to go to bed as early as a three-year-old."*** (It is important the child sees that the consequence fits the behavior.)

10. Say, ***"I hope you choose to control your anger by going to the Anger Center. We certainly do not want you to go to bed early. We like to spend time with you in the evening. If you choose to go to bed early, that is less time we will have together that evening."***

11. Say, ***"I know you can control your anger by saying, 'I am so angry because ...,' and then going to the Anger Center."***

12. Say, ***"When you choose to control yourself and pick from the Fun Jar*** (or whatever reward you have chosen)***, you will get to make important decisions or choose more grown-up things to do."***

13. Say, ***"I am very proud of you for listening. Let's celebrate our new plan by ________________________. We can call __________________ (grandparents, aunts, uncles, etc.) and tell them about our plan or we can keep it to ourselves. It's your choice."***

FUN JAR POSITIVE REINFORCEMENT IDEAS

Cut out the strips below and review each one with your child. Then fold the strips and place them in a jar. Your child may decorate the jar.

Choose what the family has for dinner.
Play a game with Mom or Dad for 20 minutes.
Read a favorite book.
Sleep in a sleeping bag anywhere in the house for one night (except Mom and Dad's room).
Be the "parent" for 15 minutes and have Mom and Dad be the "children."
Help make dinner.
Choose a special snack.
Stay up 10 minutes past your bedtime for one night.
Draw a silly picture to put on the refrigerator.
Make a 10-minute long-distance phone call with your parent's permission.
Help Mom or Dad run a fun errand.
Make a necklace or key chain out of paperclips, macaroni, etc.
Choose a song for the family to dance to.
Have an extra dessert.
For one day, choose what time you want to do your homework.
Do a special chore you do not normally do.

NO FUN JAR CONSEQUENCE IDEAS

Discuss each of the consequences below with your child. You may want to add several of your own. Since all families are unique, the consequences below may not be appropriate for your child. If this is so, you may want to modify the list to fit the needs of your family. Cut out the strips below, then fold the strips and place them in a *No Fun Jar*. Your child may decorate the jar.

No bedtime story.
No computer time.
No television for one evening.
No video games for one evening.
Go to your room for 20 minutes (no radio, television, computer, etc.).
Do a chore for Mom or Dad for 15 minutes without complaining.
Clean out your closet or someone else's closet without complaining.
Go to bed 15 minutes early … lights out!
Go to bed 30 minutes early … lights out!
Go to bed 20 minutes early … lights out!
No dessert or nighttime snack.
Ten minutes in a "time-out" chair. (If you talk or get up, your time starts over.)
Clean out a drawer in the kitchen or wherever Mom or Dad chooses.
Do a chore for Mom or Dad for 10 minutes without complaining.
No video games for one day.

NO MORE WORRIES

Complete this sheet. When you finish, fold it and put it in the *Worry Box* so all of your worries are out of your head and in the box. If you want to worry about them again, take them out of the box and talk about them with an adult.

1. What are you thinking about right now? List each thing you are worried about.

____

____

2. Do you think, in your heart, these things could ***really*** happen? Why or why not?

____

____

____

3. Does worrying about these things help you? Why or why not?

____

____

____

4. Look around the room and find five things that make you smile. You can list them below or just think about them.

____

____

____

____

____

5. Turn this paper over and list 20 things that make you smile.

GROUPS

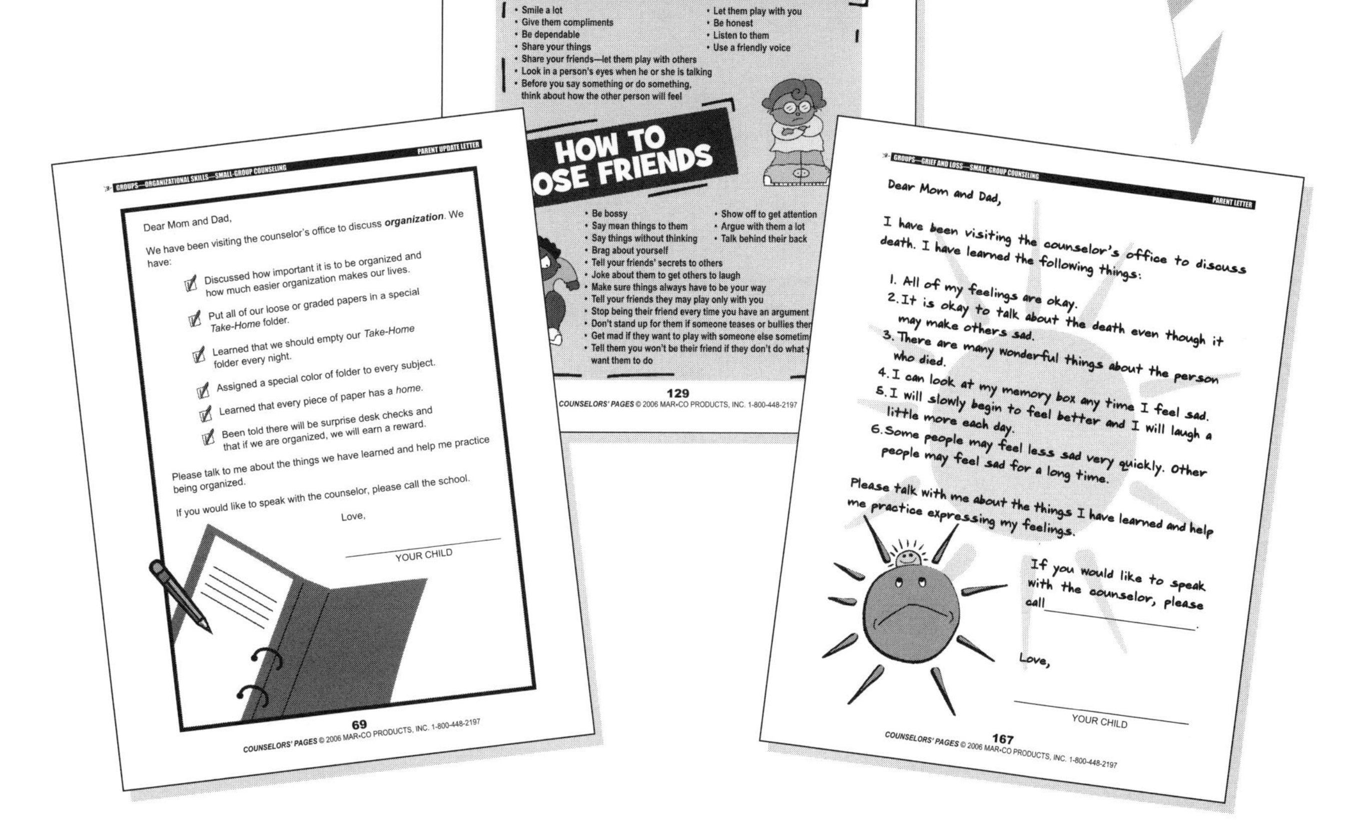
GROUPS—FRIENDSHIP—SMALL-GROUP COUNSELING/CLASSROOM GUIDANCE
STUDENT HANDOUT

FRIENDSHIP

Directions: Be TOTALLY HONEST with yourself! Circle the following things that you do to make friends and the things that you may do that cause you to lose friends.

HOW TO MAKE FRIENDS

- Smile a lot
- Give them compliments
- Be dependable
- Share your things
- Share your friends—let them play with others
- Look in a person's eyes when he or she is talking
- Before you say something or do something, think about how the other person will feel
- Let them play with you
- Be honest
- Listen to them
- Use a friendly voice

HOW TO LOSE FRIENDS

- Be bossy
- Say mean things to them
- Say things without thinking
- Brag about yourself
- Tell your friends' secrets to others
- Joke about them to get others to laugh
- Make sure things always have to be your way
- Tell your friends they may play only with you
- Stop being their friend every time you have an argument
- Don't stand up for them if someone teases or bullies them
- Get mad if they want to play with someone else sometimes
- Tell them you won't be their friend if they don't do what you want them to do
- Show off to get attention
- Argue with them a lot
- Talk behind their back

129

COUNSELORS' PAGES © 2006 MAR•CO PRODUCTS, INC. 1-800-448-2197

GROUPS—ORGANIZATIONAL SKILLS—SMALL-GROUP COUNSELING
PARENT UPDATE LETTER

Dear Mom and Dad,

We have been visiting the counselor's office to discuss ***organization***. We have:

- Discussed how important it is to be organized and how much easier organization makes our lives.
- Put all of our loose or graded papers in a special *Take-Home* folder.
- Learned that we should empty our *Take-Home* folder every night.
- Assigned a special color of folder to every subject.
- Learned that every piece of paper has a *home*.
- Been told there will be surprise desk checks and that if we are organized, we will earn a reward.

Please talk to me about the things we have learned and help me practice being organized.

If you would like to speak with the counselor, please call the school.

Love,

YOUR CHILD

69

COUNSELORS' PAGES © 2006 MAR•CO PRODUCTS, INC. 1-800-448-2197

GROUPS—GRIEF AND LOSS—SMALL-GROUP COUNSELING
PARENT LETTER

Dear Mom and Dad,

I have been visiting the counselor's office to discuss death. I have learned the following things:

1. All of my feelings are okay.
2. It is okay to talk about the death even though it may make others sad.
3. There are many wonderful things about the person who died.
4. I can look at my memory box any time I feel sad.
5. I will slowly begin to feel better and I will laugh a little more each day.
6. Some people may feel less sad very quickly. Other people may feel sad for a long time.

Please talk with me about the things I have learned and help me practice expressing my feelings.

If you would like to speak with the counselor, please call ________.

Love,

YOUR CHILD

167

COUNSELORS' PAGES © 2006 MAR•CO PRODUCTS, INC. 1-800-448-2197

GETTING STARTED

SMALL-GROUP COUNSELING

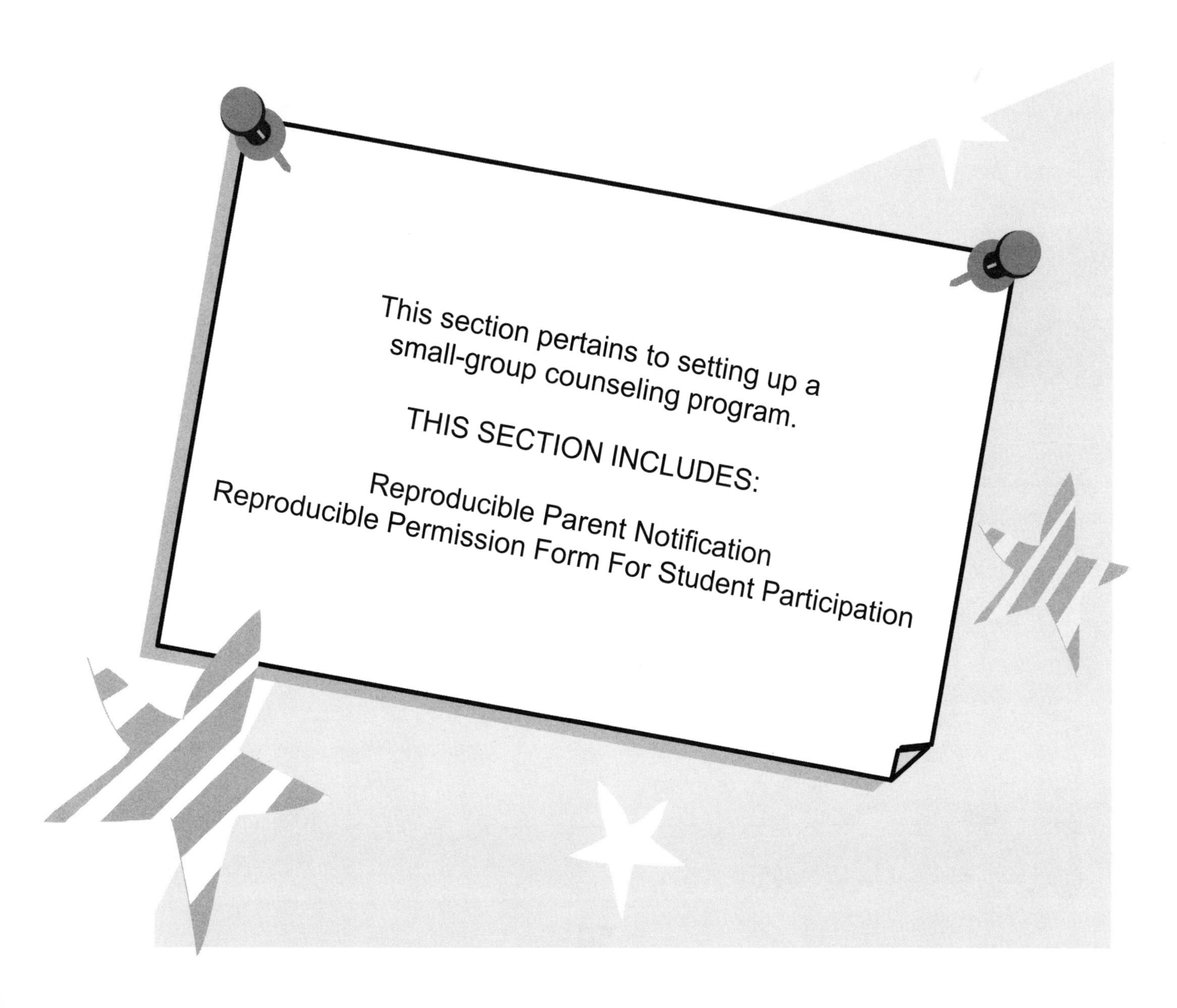

Parent Letter With
Small-Group Counseling Descriptions (pages 59-60) **SG PH**

This letter is designed to inform parents of the counseling groups offered and gives a brief description of each.

Parent Permission and Registration Form (page 61) **SG PH**

This form is enclosed with the previous letter and, when completed, returned to the counselor.

Dear Parents:

I will be initiating small-group counseling sessions during the next month. These groups will meet once a week for _____ minutes during the school day. The groups will meet for _____ to _____ sessions. These sessions may not be in consecutive weeks, due to field trips, assemblies, holidays, etc.

If you feel your child is having difficulty in one of the following areas and it is interfering with your child's academics, please sign the attached permission form and return it to your child's teacher by ______________________________. The first group sessions will begin as soon as an appropriate schedule is worked out with your child's classroom teacher.

The groups and their descriptions:

1. **Anger Management**—We will discuss why we get angry and what happens if we act out those feelings inappropriately. Participants will learn appropriate ways to express anger and that it is perfectly okay to be angry as long as the feelings are dealt with without hurting others, without hurting oneself, and without breaking things.
2. **Divorce**—We will discuss the positive and negative things about divorce. We will explain that divorce is not the child's fault and that many others are experiencing the same feelings he/she is having. We will talk about what to do if parents argue and why children should not take sides when that happens.
3. **Self-Esteem**—We will discuss the meaning of *self-esteem* and the difference between high and low self-esteem. We will discuss that the way we feel about ourselves is something we choose.
4. **Loss**—We will discuss our loss and the stages of grief. We will learn that all of our feelings are okay. We will make a memory page or a memory box about the loved one we have lost.
5. **Bullying**—This group is for students who feel bullied or picked on by other students. We will discuss ways to stand up for ourselves by using appropriate words and confident body language.
6. **Desk, Book Bag, and Folder Organization**—For this group, each student will need to bring six new pocket folders in red, yellow, blue, purple, orange, and green (or a close variation of these colors). The folders must be at school by ___________ for the student to be able to participate in this group.
7. **Friendship**—We will discuss specific behaviors that may keep students from getting along with their friends and ways to substitute appropriate behaviors. Participants will learn how to make new friends.

over➡

Due to limited time and to the overwhelming response to past groups, **please register your child for the group in which you feel he/she has the most difficulty and that deals with problems that directly influence your child's learning.** I would like very much to counsel each and every child in numerous groups, but time does not permit more than one group per child.

If you are interested in your child participating in group counseling, please complete the enclosed registration letter by checking the group you feel will be most beneficial to your child and returning the signed form to your child's teacher.

For this round of groups, all forms must be turned in by ________________________.

I will be offering the same groups throughout the year. For these later groups, the registration deadline is ______________________. Please return your form by ___________________ to reserve a space in one of those groups for your child.

I would like to help you and your child make the rest of the school year as successful as possible. If you would like to discuss your child or if you have any questions or concerns, please do not hesitate to contact me.

Sincerely,

____

INDIVIDUAL AND SMALL-GROUP COUNSELING PERMISSION AND REGISTRATION FORM

PLEASE READ THE GROUP DESCRIPTIONS CAREFULLY BEFORE REGISTERING YOUR CHILD.

I, ________________________________, give permission for my child to participate in the following counseling group with the counselor. (If your child has a great need for more than one of the following groups, please contact me so we can discuss your child's individual needs.)

Anger Management K-2nd _____ 3rd-5th _____

Divorce K-2nd _____ 3rd-5th _____

Self-Esteem K-2nd _____ 3rd-5th _____

Grief K-2nd _____ 3rd-5th _____

Bullying K-2nd _____ 3rd-5th _____
(Victims of bullying)

Organization K-2nd _____ 3rd-5th _____
(Folders described in the letter are needed for the first group session.)

Friendship K-2nd _____ 3rd-5th _____

I give permission for the counselor to see my child individually regarding the following problem:

____

____

____

Child's Name ________________________________ Date ______________

School ____________________ Grade ________ Teacher ______________

Home Phone (______) ______________ Work Phone (______) ______________

Parent's Printed Name ______________ Parent's Signature ______________

ORGANIZATIONAL SKILLS

SMALL-GROUP COUNSELING

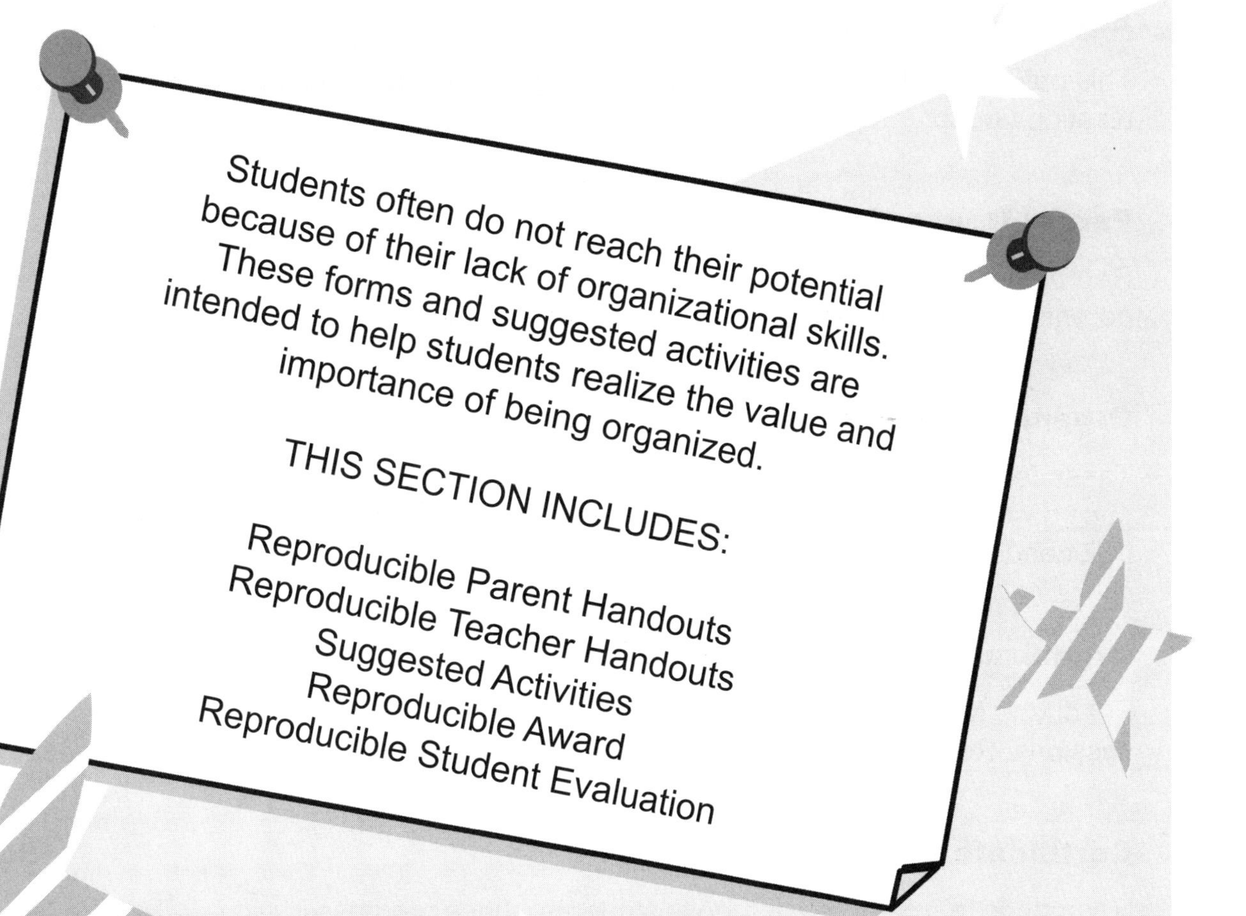

Parental Permission Form (page 65) **PH**

This letter explains the purpose of the Organization Group to parents and provides a permission slip to be signed and returned to the counselor.

Pre-Group Parental Notification Form (page 66) **PH**

Reproduce this form for all parents whose children will be participating in the Organization Group. It notifies them of their child's inclusion, supplies needed, and the time of the group meeting.

Student Evaluation Form (page 67) **TH**

This form is distributed prior to the first session of the group. It gives teachers an opportunity to tell the counselor which organizational skills the student needs to improve. It can also be adapted and filled out by parents to let the counselor know what homework skills need improvement.

Suggested Organization Activities Grades 1-5 (page 68) **IND SG SA**

This guide includes three suggested activities for use with students participating in the Organization Group.

Parent Update Letter (page 69) **PH**

Reproduce this letter and have the students sign it and take it home. This will inform the parents about what their children are learning in the group.

Organization Updates (pages 70-71) **TH**

These forms given to teachers of the students in the Organization Group should be filled out once a week to keep the counselor informed of each student's progress and identify the skills that need improvement.

Organization Group Student Evaluation (page 72) **SG SH**

Feedback from students is an invaluable resource that helps counselors plan future group sessions. Reproduce and distribute the evaluation sheet at the final group meeting.

Certificate Of Graduation (page 73) **SG SH**

Reproduce this certificate for those students whose progress is recorded on the *Organization Updates* (pages 70-71) completed by the teachers and as explained in *Suggested Activity #3* (page 68).

Dear Parents:

I will be initiating ORGANIZATION small-group counseling sessions in the next month. During these sessions, we will discuss how to categorize papers, how each paper has a "home," and how to color-code subject materials.

These sessions will meet once a week for ________ weeks. The ___-minute group may not be held on consecutive weeks, due to field trips, assemblies, holidays, etc.

If you feel a lack of organizational skills is interfering with your child's academics, please sign the following permission form and return it to your child's teacher by ____________________________. The first group session will begin as soon as an appropriate schedule is worked out with your child's classroom teacher.

I would like to help you and your child make the rest of the school year as successful as possible. If you would like to discuss your child, or you have any questions or concerns, please do not hesitate to contact me.

Sincerely,

____

WE CARE ABOUT KIDS

I, ___________________________________, give permission for my child to participate in the ORGANIZATION GROUP with the counselor.

Child's Name ____________________________________ Date __________

School ____________________________________ Grade __________

Teacher ____________________________________

Home Phone (_______) ____________________________

Work Phone (_______) ____________________________

Parent's Printed Name ____________________________

Parent's Signature ____________________________

Dear Parents,

Your child has been registered for the Organization Group. The meetings begin next week.

Your child will need six brand new pocket folders so he/she can make a fresh start when cleaning out his/her desk and getting organized. The folders should be in as many different colors as possible. Please tell your child to bring the folders to school no later than next ______________________.

The group will meet on ______________________ at ________ for the next ________ weeks. Each session will last ____ minutes. Your child's teacher has given permission for ______________________ to be excused from his/her class because the teacher feels that being more organized will improve your child's academic progress.

If you have any questions, please call me at (______)______________.

Sincerely,

STUDENT EVALUATION FORM

Dear Teachers:

Please check the items below that are causing the most difficulty for ______________________ .
I understand this student is having organization/ homework problems and I'd like to help.

Thank you,

____

- ☐ Forgets materials
- ☐ Is not ready to work when the bell rings
- ☐ Is inattentive and easily distracted
- ☐ Is often confused about what to do
- ☐ Has trouble remembering information like:

  ____

- ☐ Has a messy desk/backpack
- ☐ Loses papers and school materials
- ☐ Turns work in late and sometimes not at all
- ☐ Does not use time efficiently
- ☐ Has trouble starting projects
- ☐ Has a poor sense of time
- ☐ Does not write assignments down accurately
- ☐ Does not write assignments down at all

SUGGESTED ORGANIZATION ACTIVITIES
GRADES 1-5

These activities may be used as guidelines for facilitating a small-group or individual counseling program.

ORGANIZATION ACTIVITY #l:

Give each child six pocket folders of different colors, a pencil, and crayons or markers. Ask the children to decide, as a group, which color folder will be their math folder. Have them write *Math* on the front of that folder. Do this for each subject. Make an additional folder labeled *Take-Home Folder.* Have the children decorate each folder with something they have learned in that subject during the school year.

ORGANIZATION ACTIVITY #2:

Have the children bring everything from their desks, cubbies, book bags, etc. (except their books) to the counseling office. Then say:

> *Put every loose piece of paper into a big pile. Put all graded papers and all papers that do not need to be at school in your Take-Home Folder. You should take this folder home every night and empty it after your parents look at the papers. You may keep any papers that are special in a box under your bed. Throw away the papers you do not want to keep.*

ORGANIZATION ACTIVITY 3:

Each week, distribute a simple checklist (see *Organization Update*, pages 70-71) asking teachers how each child in your group is doing with regard to organizational skills. The checklist should include the child's progress in keeping a neater desk, finding materials and supplies more readily, and coming to class prepared. After the checklists are returned to you, go over them with each child. You may wish to have a child who has improved choose a prize from a box kept in the counseling office (preferably such school supplies as a cool eraser, pencil, etc.). If the teacher says the child has improved for three weeks in a row, give the child a certificate of graduation (page 73) from the group. If the teacher says the child continues to have difficulty in a specific area, review that concept with the child and continue to see the child weekly until the teacher reports improvement for three consecutive weeks.

Dear Mom and Dad,

We have been visiting the counselor's office to discuss organization. We have:

- ☑ Discussed how important it is to be organized and how much easier organization makes our lives.
- ☑ Put all of our loose or graded papers in a special Take-Home Folder.
- ☑ Learned that we should empty our Take-Home Folder every night.
- ☑ Assigned a special color of folder to every subject.
- ☑ Learned that every piece of paper has a home.
- ☑ Been told there will be surprise desk checks and that if we are organized, we will earn a reward.

Please talk to me about the things we have learned and help me practice being organized.

If you would like to speak with the counselor, please call the school.

Love,

____

YOUR CHILD

ORGANIZATION UPDATE

Please check how ______________________________ is doing with organization and return this slip to me before our next session on _______________________ .

1. **Is his/her desk/area neater and cleaner?**

   ☐ YES ☐ NO ☐ NO PREVIOUS PROBLEM

2. **Is it easier for him/her to find papers?**

   ☐ YES ☐ NO ☐ NO PREVIOUS PROBLEM

3. **Is homework being turned in on time?**

   ☐ YES ☐ NO ☐ NO PREVIOUS PROBLEM

Thank you,

____

ORGANIZATION UPDATE

Please check how ______________________________ is doing with organization and return this slip to me before our next session on _______________________ .

1. **Is his/her desk/area neater and cleaner?**

   ☐ YES ☐ NO ☐ NO PREVIOUS PROBLEM

2. **Is it easier for him/her to find papers?**

   ☐ YES ☐ NO ☐ NO PREVIOUS PROBLEM

3. **Is homework being turned in on time?**

   ☐ YES ☐ NO ☐ NO PREVIOUS PROBLEM

Thank you,

____

ORGANIZATION UPDATE

Please check how ________________________________ is doing with organization this week. Please return this form to me before our next session on ______________________. Thank you for taking the time.

1. **Clean desk**
   ☐ YES ☐ NO ☐ NEVER HAD A PROBLEM
2. **Can find papers**
   ☐ YES ☐ NO ☐ NEVER HAD A PROBLEM
3. **Is prepared with correct materials and supplies**
   ☐ YES ☐ NO ☐ NEVER HAD A PROBLEM
4. **Turns homework in on time**
   ☐ YES ☐ NO ☐ NEVER HAD A PROBLEM
5. **Brings notes, folders, etc. back to school on time**
   ☐ YES ☐ NO ☐ NEVER HAD A PROBLEM

ORGANIZATION UPDATE

Please check how ________________________________ is doing with organization this week. Please return this form to me before our next session on ______________________. Thank you for taking the time.

1. **Clean desk**
   ☐ YES ☐ NO ☐ NEVER HAD A PROBLEM
2. **Can find papers**
   ☐ YES ☐ NO ☐ NEVER HAD A PROBLEM
3. **Is prepared with correct materials and supplies**
   ☐ YES ☐ NO ☐ NEVER HAD A PROBLEM
4. **Turns homework in on time**
   ☐ YES ☐ NO ☐ NEVER HAD A PROBLEM
5. **Brings notes, folders, etc. back to school on time**
   ☐ YES ☐ NO ☐ NEVER HAD A PROBLEM

ORGANIZATION GROUP STUDENT EVALUATION

NAME ______________________________ DATE ____________

TEACHER ______________________________

Please answer the following questions about the Organization Group **HONESTLY**:

1. I enjoyed coming to the counselor's office. (Please circle one.)

   A LOT **A LITTLE** **NOT AT ALL**

2. I learned things in this group that I didn't already know. (Please circle one.)

   A LOT **A LITTLE** **NOT AT ALL**

3. The thing I liked best about this group was:

   ____

   ____

4. The thing I didn't like about this group was:

   ____

   ____

5. Three (3) things I learned in this group were:

   A. ______________________________

   ____

   B. ______________________________

   ____

   C. ______________________________

   ____

6. I would like to be a member of another group with the counselor. (Please circle one.)

   A LOT **A LITTLE** **NOT AT ALL**

____

has demonstrated
marked improvement in

ORGANIZATIONAL SKILLS

and is thereby an official graduate
of the Organization Group.

____

COUNSELOR

BULLYING

SMALL-GROUP COUNSELING
CLASSROOM GUIDANCE

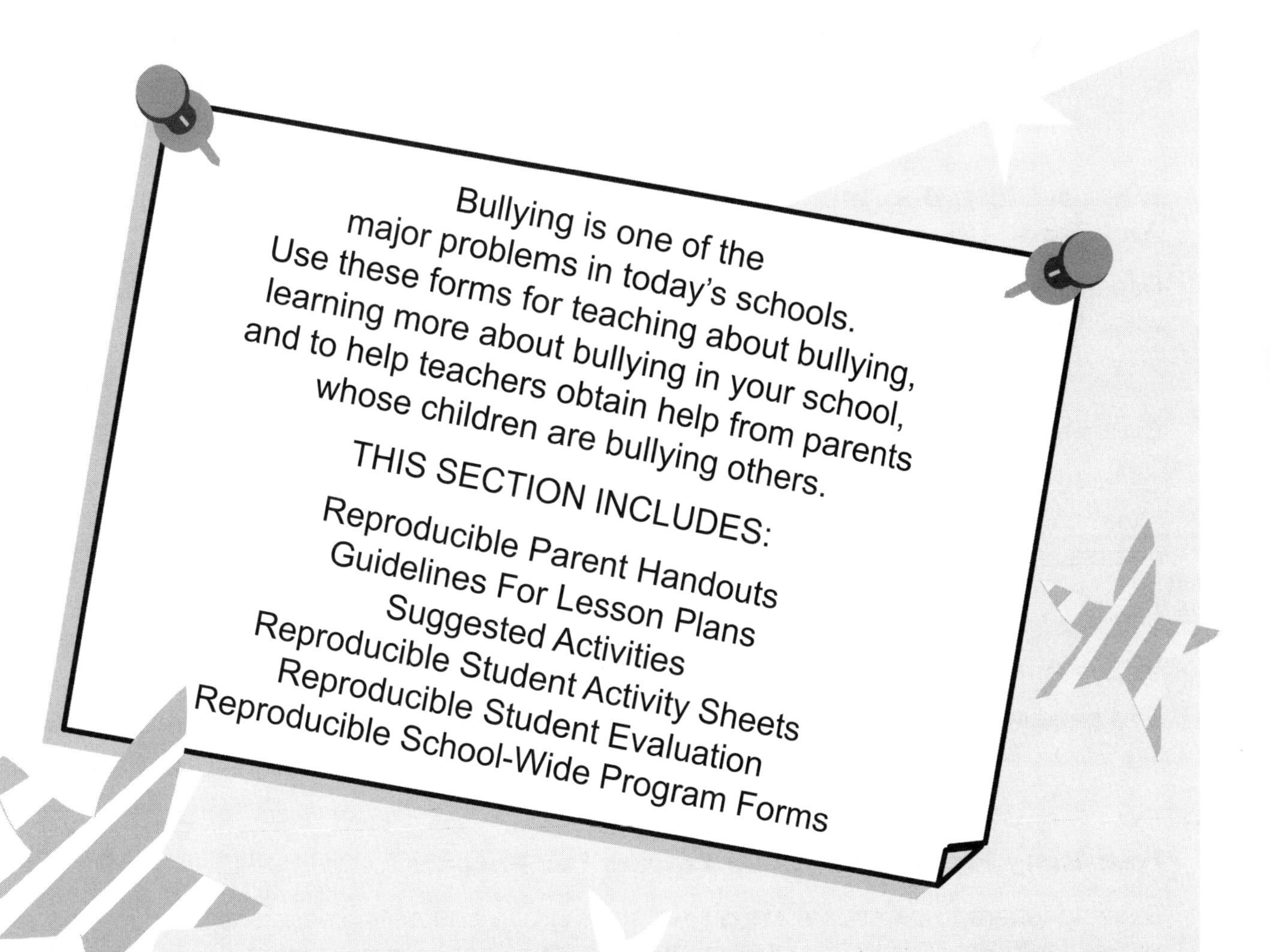

Bully Prevention Group Parent Permission Form (page 78) **SG PH**

Distribute this sheet to parents of all children in the targeted grade levels.

Student Evaluation Form (page 79) **TH**

This form, given to teachers prior to the first session of the group, provides an opportunity for them to tell the counselor bullying behaviors which need to be addressed with the student.

Bullying Lesson Plan Grades K-2 (pages 80-81) **SG CG**

A sample lesson plan for use either with small groups or in the classroom.

Bullying Lesson Plan Grades 3-5 (pages 82-83) **SG CG**

A sample lesson plan for use either with small groups or in the classroom.

Bully, Doormat, And Stand-Upper Role-Play Cards (pages 84-85) **SG CG**

Reproduce and cut apart enough cards so each student in the group will have a card.

What A Bully, Doormat,
And Stand-Upper Might Say (page 86) **SG CG SH**

Use this activity sheet in the Grade K-2 Bully Lesson Plan or at any time to give examples of what the bully, doormat, or stand-upper might say.

Bullies, Doormats, And Stand-Uppers (page 87) **IND SG CG SH**

Distribute this sheet to each student. Then explain the information written on it. This activity sheet can be used in the K-2 and 3-5 Bully Lesson Plans or as a springboard for further discussion about bullies and their behaviors and about reactions to bullying behaviors.

Suggested Bullying Activities Grades 1-5 (page 88) **SG SA**

This page includes three suggested activities for use with students participating in the Bullying Group.

Post-Bully Prevention Group Letters For Parents (pages 89-90) **SG PH**

Sending letters to parents at the end of small-group counseling sessions is courteous and appreciated. Either of the two letters found on these pages is appropriate.

Bully Prevention Group Student Evaluation Form (page 91) **SG SH**

Feedback from students is an invaluable resource that helps counselors plan future group sessions. Distribute the evaluation sheet at the final group meeting.

Parent Interview (page 92) **IND SG CG SH**

Bullying is not new. It has occurred through the ages. Distribute this sheet to the students. Tell them to take the paper home, ask their parents the questions, write down their answers, and return the paper to you for discussion. This activity makes children aware that their parents may have faced the same issues as they do in elementary school.

Bully Busters (page 93) **IND SG CG SH**

Students who are being bullied need to feel a sense of power. Distribute this sheet to help victims realize that they have many choices and the power to stop the bullying.

Bully Buster Box Letter (page 94) **SW**

Place a mailbox called the *Bully Buster Box* outside of your office. Tell the students that anyone who feels bullied may inform the counselor by placing a letter in the box. The letter should include the bully's name, a description of what the bully did, and the name of the person being bullied. Using the form on page 94, the counselor will then inform the bully, without using the victim's name, that the counselor is aware of the situation.

Unkind Report Form (page 95) **SW PH**

Reproduce this form and distribute it to those teachers who wish to use it when a student is unkind to another student. The forms are kept by the teacher and sent home at the teacher's discretion.

Bully Prevention Award (page 96) **IND SG CG SH**

Reproduce one of these awards for any student who is seen standing up for him/herself or others in a potential bullying situation.

Dear Parents,

I will be initiating BULLY PREVENTION small-group counseling sessions in the next month. During these sessions, we will discuss the meaning of *bullying* and what it means to be a *bully*, a *victim*, a *doormat*, and a *stand-upper*. In addition, we will discuss strategies students can use to stand up to bullies.

These sessions will meet once a week for ________ weeks. The ___-minute group may not be held on consecutive weeks, due to field trips, assemblies, holidays, etc.

If you feel bullying is interfering with your child's academics, please sign the following permission form and return it to your child's teacher by _____________. The first group session will begin as soon as an appropriate schedule is worked out with your child's classroom teacher.

I would like to help you and your child make the rest of the school year as successful as possible. If you would like to discuss your child, or you have any questions or concerns, please do not hesitate to contact me.

Sincerely,

____

WE CARE ABOUT KIDS

- -

I, ___________________________________, give permission for my child to participate in the BULLY PREVENTION GROUP with the counselor.

Child's Name ___________________________________ Date ___________

School ____ Grade __________

Teacher _______________________________________

Home Phone (_______) __________________________

Work Phone (_______) __________________________

Parent's Printed Name __________________________

Parent's Signature _____________________________

STUDENT EVALUATION FORM

Dear Teachers:

Please check the items below that are causing the most difficulty for ______________________ . I understand this student is having problems either as a victim or a bully and I'd like to help.

Thank you,

____

- [ ] Frequently puts other students down
- [ ] Has low self-esteem
- [ ] Verbally or physically threatens other students
- [ ] Is frequently picked on by other students
- [ ] Cannot handle a situation in which he/she is bullied
- [ ] Is disliked by most students
- [ ] Frequently teases certain children
- [ ] Has a strong influence on other students
- [ ] Appears frightened during recess or when going home from school
- [ ] Gossips about other students
- [ ] Thinks he/she is better than other students
- [ ] Physically attacks other students

BULLYING LESSON PLAN
GRADES K-2

The following bullying lesson plan may be used as a guideline for one session in a small-group counseling or classroom-guidance program.

Materials Needed:

- ☐ Chalkboard and chalk, dry-erase board and marker
- ☐ *Bully, Doormat, And Stand-Upper Role-Play Cards* (pages 84-85)
- ☐ Copy of *What A Bully, Doormat, And Stand-Upper Might Say* (page 86)
- ☐ Copy of *Bullies, Doormats, And Stand-Uppers* (page 87) for each student

Pre-Presentation Preparation:

Write on the board:

BULLY (draw an angry face)—someone who tries to talk you into doing something that you know in your heart is wrong

DOORMAT (draw a frightened face)—someone who does whatever a bully tells him/her to do even though he/she knows it is wrong

STAND-UPPER (draw a happy face)—someone who does what he/she knows is right and stands up to a bully

Reproduce *Bully, Doormat, And Stand-Upper Role-Play Cards.* Cut the cards apart. Laminate them for durability.

Reproduce *What A Bully, Doormat, And Stand-Upper Might Say* for the leader.

Reproduce *Bullies, Doormats, And Stand-Uppers* for each student.

Presentation:

- Have the students sit in a circle on the floor, legs crossed.
- Have the students take turns saying their name and telling what their favorite foods are.
- Ask the students, "Do you know what a bully is?" *(Allow time for responses.)* Then discuss the definition of *bully* written on the board.

- Give several examples of what a bully might do, such as tell others not to play with someone, tease or call someone names, physically hurt someone, etc.

- Ask the students, “Do you know what a doormat is?” *(Allow time for responses.)* Then discuss the definition of *doormat* written on the board.

- Give examples of what a doormat might say such as, “Okay, I’ll do whatever you say,” or “Even though I know it’s wrong and mean, I’ll tease that girl if you want me to,” or “Even though it will hurt his feelings, I’ll tell him he can’t play soccer if you want me to do that.”

- Ask the students, “Do you know what a stand-upper is?” *(Allow time for responses.).* Then discuss the definition of *stand-upper* written on the board.

- Give examples of a stand-upper such as someone who tells the bully to stop teasing him/her, someone who tells the bully to stop teasing another child, or someone who gets a group of friends together to tell the bully to stop whatever he/she is doing.

- Tell the students they are going to role-play. Explain that they will come to the front of the room, one at a time, and draw a card from the pile. Bully, doormat, or stand-upper will be written on each card. After the card is drawn, you will whisper a statement to the student that corresponds with the category on his/her card. They will then repeat the statement to the group. The group will guess which role the student is acting out.

- Ask for volunteers.

- Have the volunteer select a card. Using *What A Bully, Doormat, And Stand-Upper Might Say,* whisper the corresponding statement to the student. Have the student repeat the statement to the group.

- Continue until each student has had a turn.

- Distribute *Bullies, Doormats, And Stand-Uppers* to each student to take home.

BULLYING LESSON PLAN
GRADES 3-5

The following bullying lesson plan may be used as a guideline for one session in a small-group counseling or classroom-guidance program.

Materials Needed:

- ☐ Chalkboard and chalk, dry-erase board and marker
- ☐ Copy of *Bullies, Doormats, And Stand-Uppers* (page 87) for each student

Pre-Presentation Preparation:

Write on the board:

BULLY (draw an angry face)—someone who tries to talk you into doing something that you know in your heart is wrong

DOORMAT (draw a frightened face)—someone who does whatever a bully tells him/her to do even though he/she knows it is wrong

STAND-UPPER (draw a happy face)—someone who does what he/she knows is right and stands up to a bully

Reproduce *Bullies, Doormats, And Stand-Uppers* for each student.

Presentation:

- Have the students sit in a circle on the floor, legs crossed.
- Have the students take turns saying their name and telling what their favorite television shows are.
- Ask the students, "Have you ever been bullied?" *(Allow time for responses.)* "What happened?" *(Allow time for responses.)* Then discuss the definition of *bully* written on the board.
- Ask the students, "Do you know what a *doormat* is?" *(Allow time for responses.)* "Without using any names, can you tell of a time when you saw someone being a *doormat*?" *(Allow time for responses.)* Then discuss the definition of *doormat* written on the board.

- Give examples of what a *doormat* might say such as, "Okay, I'll do whatever you say," or "Even though I know it's wrong and mean, I'll tease that girl if you want me to," or "Even though it will hurt his feelings, I'll tell him he can't play soccer if you want me to do that."

- Ask the students, "Do you know of or have you seen others standing up for someone or themselves?" *(Allow time for responses.)* Then discuss the definition of *stand-upper* written on the board.

- Give examples of a *stand-upper* such as someone who tells the *bully* to stop teasing him/her, someone who tells the *bully* to stop teasing someone else, or someone who gets a group of friends together to tell the *bully* to stop what he/she is doing.

- Tell the students you are going to divide them into groups of three for role-playing. In the groups, they are to choose one *bully*, one *doormat*, and one *stand-upper*. Then they are to make up a skit with each person in the group portraying the role he/she has been assigned. The rest of the group is to guess which role each student is portraying. The students will have 10 minutes to prepare their skits.

- Assign the groups.

- After 10 minutes, have each group act out its skit. When all of the groups have performed, applaud their presentations.

- Distribute *Bullies, Doormats, And Stand-Uppers* to each student to take home.

BULLY, DOORMAT, AND STAND-UPPER ROLE-PLAY CARDS

BULLY	BULLY
BULLY	BULLY
BULLY	BULLY
BULLY	BULLY
DOORMAT	DOORMAT
DOORMAT	DOORMAT

BULLY, DOORMAT, AND STAND-UPPER ROLE-PLAY CARDS

DOORMAT	DOORMAT
DOORMAT	DOORMAT
STAND-UPPER	STAND-UPPER
STAND-UPPER	STAND-UPPER
STAND-UPPER	STAND-UPPER
STAND-UPPER	STAND-UPPER

WHAT A BULLY, DOORMAT, AND STAND-UPPER MIGHT SAY

A BULLY MIGHT SAY...

- Let's not play with him.
- Don't talk to her.
- Go tell her she doesn't belong with us.
- Don't be his friend.
- You can play only with me and no one else.
- It's your fault we lost the game.

A DOORMAT MIGHT SAY...

- I won't play with him if you don't want me to.
- No one wants to talk to her so I won't, either.
- I'll go tell him he doesn't belong with us if you want me to do that.
- If you don't want me to be her friend, I won't.
- I'll play only with you if you don't want me to have any other friends.
- It's okay with me if we take his lunch money. You're the boss.

A STAND-UPPER MIGHT SAY...

- I want to play with everyone who wants to play.
- I want to talk to her because if I don't, that will hurt her feelings.
- You can play with me any time.
- I share my friends, so you can play with whomever you'd like.
- I don't play with just one person. I like to include everyone.
- What you want me to do isn't right, and I won't go along with you.

BULLIES, DOORMATS, AND STAND-UPPERS

There are three kinds of people:

BULLY

A person who tries to talk you into doing something that you know in your heart is not right.

DOORMAT

Someone who does whatever a bully says to do or stands back and does not help someone who is being teased or bullied.

STAND-UPPER

Someone who does what he/she knows is right and stands up to a bully.

SUGGESTED BULLYING ACTIVITIES
GRADES 1-5

BULLYING ACTIVITY #I:

Have the students discuss times they have felt teased, taunted, or bullied and how they felt before, during, and after each episode. Then say:

> *People feel bullied when they do not feel they have the power to prevent a situation. Think about your situation. What do you wish you could have said or done?*
>
> *Having power does not mean hurting someone's feelings or body, but feeling like you can stand up for yourself and ask for help if you need it.*

Distribute drawing paper and crayons or markers. Then have each child draw a picture of him/herself as a superhero. On the top of each page, have each child write *I Have Power!*

BULLYING ACTIVITY #2:

Show the children what a victim's body looks like. For example, eyes looking down, shoulders slumped, feet not firmly planted on the ground, body swaying, and soft voice. Have each child represent a part of the body. One child will be the eyes, another the shoulders, another the feet, another the voice, etc. Tell each of the participating children to show how his/her body part should look when speaking to a bully. Then have each child represent all the body parts and role-play standing up to a bully.

BULLYING ACTIVITY #3:

Discuss ways to confront a bully. Have the students develop strategies for standing up to a bully, like getting a group of friends to help, writing the bully a letter, calling the bully on the phone and asking him/her to please stop, saying "Thank you" whenever the bully teases, etc. Have the students choose one of the *Bully Busters* (page 93) and act it out while the rest of the group decides what strategy is used in the skit.

Dear Parents:

Your child has been coming to the counseling office to discuss ways to prevent bullying. We have discussed the following things about bullies:

1. A bully is someone who tries to talk you into doing something you know in your heart is not right.
2. A bully usually wants power over you.
3. A victim is someone who gets treated badly by a bully.
4. A doormat is someone who does whatever a bully wants him/her to do even though he/she knows it is wrong.
5. A stand-upper is someone who stands up for him/herself or for someone else.
6. There are many things you can try to do to handle a bully, such as walking away, telling the bully how you feel when the two of you are alone in a safe place, confronting the bully with a group of your friends in a safe place, or saying “Thank you” every time the bully says something rude to you.
7. You always have power over bullying!
8. Never just put up with bullying. If you have tried lots of things and they have not worked, keep telling adults until someone helps you!

In our group, we have role-played many bullying scenarios. Please continue to practice these skills with your child.

After the final session of this group, the children know they may visit with me by writing a letter or telling their teacher they want to talk with me. If I can help you or your child again, please let me know.

Sincerely,

Dear Mom and Dad,

We have been visiting the counselor's office to discuss being bullied. We have learned the following things:

1. No one has the right to treat me badly.
2. I have power over bullies.
3. I can stand up for myself by looking the bully in the eye and saying I do not like being treated badly.
4. I can get a group of my friends together to confront the bully with me.
5. It is perfectly okay to ask an adult for help.
6. My body language can tell a bully to leave me alone.

Please talk with me about the things we have learned and help me practice standing up for myself.

If you would like to speak with the counselor, please call:

(______)________________.

Love,

____

YOUR CHILD

STOP BULLYING

BULLY PREVENTION GROUP STUDENT EVALUATION

NAME ______________________________ DATE ____________

TEACHER ______________________________

Please answer the following questions about the Bully Prevention Group **HONESTLY**:

1. I enjoyed coming to the counselor's office. (Please circle one.)

   A LOT **A LITTLE** **NOT AT ALL**

2. I learned things in this group that I didn't already know. (Please circle one.)

   A LOT **A LITTLE** **NOT AT ALL**

3. The thing I liked best about this group was:

   ____

   ____

4. The thing I didn't like about this group was:

   ____

   ____

5. Three (3) things I learned in this group were:

   A. ______________________________

   ____

   B. ______________________________

   ____

   C. ______________________________

   ____

6. I would like to be a member of another group with the counselor. (Please circle one.)

   A LOT **A LITTLE** **NOT AT ALL**

PARENT INTERVIEW

(Parent's Homework)

Directions: Ask one or both of your parents for a few minutes of their time. Tell them you are studying about *bullying* at school and want to ask them about *bullying* when they were in school and for advice. Write their answers on the lines after each question.

Due to the Counselor: One week from today, on ____________________ .

1. Please tell me a story about bullying when you were around my age.

   ____
   ____
   ____

2. Have you ever been bullied? ______________________________

   What did you do about it? ______________________________
   ____

   How did you feel about it then? ______________________________
   ____

   How do you feel about it now? ______________________________
   ____

3. If someone were bullying me, what advice would you give me? __________
   ____
   ____
   ____

4. Do you think bullying can be stopped? ______________________________

   If yes, how? If not, why? ______________________________
   ____
   ____

BULLY BUSTERS

When someone is treating you badly, YOU have lots of choices!

You have power over the situation. Decide to do one of the following choices. If it doesn't stop the bullying, choose another one, and so on.

1. Keep things the way they are right now.
2. Tell the person how you feel.
3. Write the person a letter.
4. Call the person and tell him/her how you feel.
5. When the person says something rude, just say, "Thank you!"
6. Ignore the person.
7. Talk to the person when your best friend or a group of friends is with you.
8. Talk to the person with the counselor and try to work things out.
9. Ask the counselor to talk with the person when you are not there.
10. Be very kind to the person whenever you see him/her.
11. Use the space below to write other solutions.

____

____

Take this list home and talk it over with your parents.
Choose a solution to try and let me know what choice you have made.

Be very proud because you came to someone for help!

NO ONE HAS THE RIGHT TO TREAT YOU BADLY.

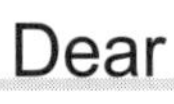

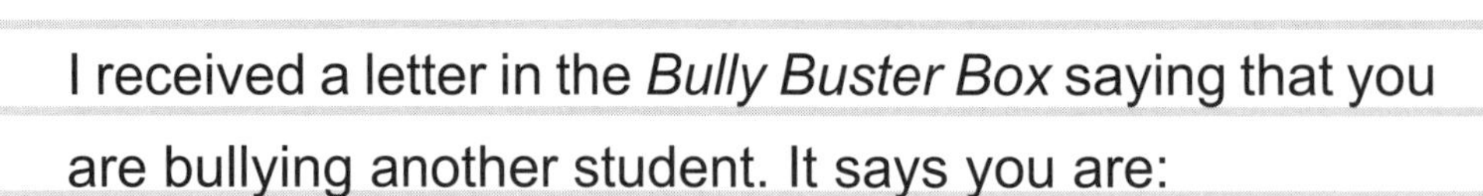

Dear ,

I received a letter in the *Bully Buster Box* saying that you are bullying another student. It says you are:

If this is true, please watch what you say and do to others, because your actions are hurtful to someone else. If this is not true and someone is trying to get you into trouble, just remember to be kind to everyone.

UNKIND REPORT

We are working on being kind to others in the classroom. Both the counselor and I have talked to the class about saying and doing nice things for others. Some students are still having trouble being kind. When your child says or does something unkind to another child, I know parents would like to be informed. Please sign this and return it tomorrow to your child's teacher. Our goal is to make sure school is a positive, a comfortable, and an enriching environment for everyone.

_______________________________ has chosen to say or do something unkind to a classmate today.

He/she has chosen to:

Teacher's Initials ________________

Date ___________________________

Please sign and return by __________

You stood up for yourself today!

Counselor____________________ Date___________

You stood up for someone else today!

Counselor____________________ Date___________

SELF•ESTEEM

SMALL-GROUP COUNSELING
CLASSROOM GUIDANCE

Without positive self-esteem, a child's friendships, academic success, social interactions, and behavior can suffer.
The following forms are supplements for a classroom or small-group counseling program.

THIS SECTION INCLUDES:

Reproducible Parent Handouts
Guidelines For Lesson Plans
Suggested Activities
Reproducible Student Activity Sheets
Reproducible Poster
Reproducible Student Evaluation

Self-Esteem Group Parent Permission Form (page 100) **SG PH**

Distribute this sheet to parents of all children in the targeted grade levels.

Student Evaluation Form (page 101) **TH**

This form, given to teachers prior to the first session, provides an opportunity for them to tell the counselor the self-esteem issues which need to be addressed with the student.

Self-Esteem Lesson Plans Grades PK-5 (pages 102-108) **SG CG**

These three sample lesson plans are guidelines for presenting material to grades PK-K, grades 1-2, and grades 3-5. Each lesson includes a step-by-step presentation guide, discussion, and interactive activities.

Suggested Self-Esteem Activities Grades 1-5 (page 109) **SG SA**

This guide includes three suggested activities for use with students participating in the Self-Esteem Group.

What I Think Others Would Say About Me (page 111) **IND SG CG SH**

This activity will help the counselor determine the student's level of self-esteem by examining the student's perception of what others think of him/her.

20 Things I Like About Me (page 112) **IND SG CG SH**

This activity will help students recognize their positive traits. It can be completed in one lesson or used in several by adding traits as they are recognized.

Parents' Self-Esteem Homework (pages 113-114) **IND SG CG SH**

Parents are among the most, if not *the* most, important persons in a child's life. To be recognized by them is a significant self-esteem booster. Reproduce the activity sheets and have each student take them home along with a return envelope. Have the students return the completed activity sheets the following week in the sealed envelope. During the counseling session, open the envelopes and read the parents' positive comments aloud.

Self-Esteem Remote Control (page 115) **IND SG CG SH**

This activity sheet will help the members of the Self-Esteem Group realize that they have control over how they feel about themselves. When presenting the activity sheet, discuss each part of the remote control and how it relates to self-esteem.

Self-Esteem Poster (page 116) **IND SG CG SH**

Reproduce this page for the students. Encourage them to post it at school or at home in a place where they will easily be reminded of its message.

Post Self-Esteem Small-Group Counseling Letter For Parents (page 117) **SG PH**

Sending letters to parents at the end of small-group counseling sessions is courteous and appreciated.

Self-Esteem Group Student Evaluation (page 118) **SG SH**

Feedback from students is an invaluable resource that helps counselors plan future group sessions. Distribute the evaluation sheet at the final group meeting.

Dear Parents:

I will be initiating SELF-ESTEEM small-group counseling sessions in the next month. During these sessions, we will discuss the meaning of *self-esteem* and the difference between high and low self-esteem. We will discuss that we choose the way we feel about ourselves. In addition, we will discuss how everyone is good at something, but no one is good at everything.

These sessions will meet once a week for ________ weeks. The ___-minute group may not be held on consecutive weeks, due to field trips, assemblies, holidays, etc.

If you feel your child's self-esteem is interfering with his/her academics, please sign the following permission form and return it to your child's teacher by ____________________________. The first group session will begin as soon as an appropriate schedule is worked out with your child's classroom teacher.

I would like to help you and your child make the rest of the school year as successful as possible. If you would like to discuss your child, or you have any questions or concerns, please do not hesitate to contact me.

Sincerely,

____

WE CARE ABOUT KIDS

- -

I, ________________________________, give permission for my child to participate in the SELF-ESTEEM GROUP with the counselor.

Child's Name ________________________________ Date __________

School ________________________________ Grade _________

Teacher ________________________________

Home Phone (_______) ________________________

Work Phone (_______) ________________________

Parent's Printed Name ________________________

Parent's Signature ________________________

STUDENT EVALUATION FORM

Dear Teachers:

Please check the items below that are causing the most difficulty for ______________________ .
I understand this student is having problems with low self-esteem and I'd like to help.

Thank you,

____

- ☐ Is overly self-critical
- ☐ Is easily influenced by the remarks of other students
- ☐ Is a "follower"
- ☐ Is picked on frequently by other students
- ☐ Cannot handle criticism
- ☐ Does not have many "true" friends
- ☐ Constantly tries to please both adults and peers
- ☐ Is often a loner
- ☐ Lacks self-confidence when given an assignment
- ☐ Waits to be asked to join games or groups
- ☐ Rarely raises hand to answer a question
- ☐ Prefers to not do an assignment, rather than do it incorrectly

SELF-ESTEEM LESSON PLAN
GRADES PK-K

Materials Needed:

- ☐ Copy of prepared book (see Pre-Presentation Preparation), pencil, sticker, and crayons for each student

Pre-Presentation Preparation:

Write the following headings on the top of each sheet of paper:

Page 1: My name is ______________________________ .
Page 2: This is what I could do well when I was one-year-old ...
Page 3: This is what I could do well when I was two-years-old...
Page 4: This is what I could do well when I was three-years-old...
Continue this procedure until you reach the students' present age.
Last page: This is what I will be able to do well when I am older...

Copy these pages for each student, then staple the pages together. These are the books the children will be creating during the lesson.

Presentation:

- Have the students sit in a circle on the floor, legs crossed.
- Have the students take turns saying their name and what their favorite food is.
- Discuss how each child is different ... their names are different, they like different foods, they look different, etc. These differences make all the children very special.
- Tell the students they are going to play a game. Explain that you are going to make some statements. If a statement you make applies to them, they are to stand. If it does not, they are to stay seated. Once they stand, they should remain standing until they hear a statement that does not apply to them. Then they should sit down until they hear another statement that applies to them.

  Stand if you have a dog.
  Stand if you have a cat.
  Stand if you have a pet bird.
  Stand if you like broccoli.
  Stand if you like flowers.
  Stand if you have a brother.
  Stand if you have a sister.

Stand if you like ice cream.
Stand if you like to go swimming.
Stand if you think you are very special.

- Have the students sit down. Then have each student tell the group two things he/she can do very well. Ask the students if they could do those things when they were one-year-old or two-years-old. Explain that every year, as they get older, they will be able to do more and more.

- Distribute a book, pencil, and crayons to each student. Explain that everyone will do this activity at the same time.

- Have the students begin by writing their names on the line on the cover of the book and then drawing a picture of themselves below their names.

- Have the students open their books to the next page. Read the heading aloud: "This is what I could do well when I was one-year-old …" Then have the students draw a picture of themselves at one, walking or smiling, waving bye-bye, etc.

- Read the next heading aloud: "This is what I could do well when I was two-years-old …" Then have the students draw a picture of themselves at two, singing, dancing, running, etc.

- Continue this procedure until the students reach their present age and they have drawn, under that picture, what they do well now.

- On the last page, read the final heading aloud: "This is what I will be able to do well when I am older …" Then have the students draw what they will be able to do well when they are older.

- When everyone has finished, go around the room and have each child share one or more of his/her pictures with the group. For example, "I could dance well," or "I will be able to swim well."

- If time permits, have the students return to the circle and read their special book to the other students.

- Allow each student to take his/her book home. Before the students leave, put a sticker on the cover of each book.

- When everyone has finished, go around the room and have each child share one or more of his/her pictures with the group. For example, "I could dance well," or "I will be able to swim well."

- If time permits, have the students return to the circle and read their special book to the other students.

- Allow each student to take his/her book home. Before the students leave, put a sticker on the cover of each book.

SELF-ESTEEM LESSON PLAN
GRADES 1-2

Materials Needed:

- ☐ Age-appropriate book on self-esteem (optional)
- ☐ Large piece of posterboard
- ☐ Marker
- ☐ Beanbag
- ☐ Copy of *Feelings* (page 106) for each student
- ☐ Crayons for each student
- ☐ Sticker for each student

Pre-Presentation Preparation:

Using the marker and posterboard, draw an exact replica of the *Feelings* activity sheet on the posterboard.

Presentation:

- Have the students sit in a circle on the floor, legs crossed.
- Ask each student to state his/her name, age, and favorite vegetable.
- Ask the students to raise their hands if they have ever felt happy. Have one student give an example of a time he/she felt happy. Repeat the procedure with the feelings *sad, mad, excited, left out,* and *scared*. If necessary, give the students examples of times you have had these feelings.
- Explain that everyone has a right to feel whatever he/she wants to feel and that it is okay to have any of these feelings. Explain it is even okay to feel *angry*, but that it is important not to hurt others' feelings or their bodies and it is not okay to break things.
- Optional: Read a book on self-esteem.
- Have the students line up according to their birthdates. All students born in January will be first, February birthdays second, etc. Then tell the students to sit down in that order.
- Place the posterboard several feet away on the floor.
- Have the students take turns throwing a beanbag onto the posterboard. Whichever feeling the bag lands on is the feeling that child must use in a sentence, like "I felt scared when my brother turned the lights out and that's okay."

- When everyone has had a turn at the beanbag game, discuss again how it is okay to have lots of feelings.

- Reinforce the fact that everyone is different and has different feelings.

- Have the students move to a table or their desks. Distribute *Feelings* and crayons to each student. Then ask:

  How would you feel if you saw a scary movie? Would you feel happy, sad, mad, excited, left out, or frightened? Draw a picture of yourself in the box under that feeling. Remember, everyone has feelings and all feelings are okay.

  How would you feel if someone said he or she wanted to be your friend? Would you feel happy, sad, mad, excited, left out, or frightened? Draw a picture of yourself in the box under that feeling. Remember, everyone has feelings and all feelings are okay.

  How would you feel if someone said you could not play a game with him or her, so you had to play alone? Would you feel happy, sad, mad, excited, left out, or frightened? Draw a picture of yourself in the box under that feeling. Remember, everyone has feelings and all feelings are okay.

  How would you feel if someone said you were going to Disneyworld next summer? Would you feel happy, sad, mad, excited, left out, or frightened? Draw a picture of yourself in the box under that feeling. Remember, everyone has feelings and all feelings are okay.

  How would you feel if your best friend was moving away to another city? Would you feel happy, sad, mad, excited, left out, or frightened? Draw a picture of yourself in the box under that feeling. Remember, everyone has feelings and all feelings are okay.

  How would you feel if someone said you could not play a game with the rest of the kids? Draw a picture of yourself in the box under that feeling. Remember, everyone has feelings and all feelings are okay."

- Have the students return to the circle with their pictures. Have them share their pictures with the group.

- Remind the students that everyone's feelings are okay whether they are the same or different from everyone else's.

- Put a sticker on each picture and allow the students to take their pictures home.

FEELINGS

HAPPY	SAD	EXCITED

SCARED	MAD	LEFT OUT

SELF-ESTEEM LESSON PLAN

GRADES 3-5

Materials Needed:

- ☐ Pencil, marker, paper, crayons, construction paper, gluestick or tape, can (coffee can or large juice can), scissors, and stickers for each student

Pre-Presentation Preparation:

Put a supply of pencils, markers, paper, crayons, construction paper, gluesticks or tape, stickers, cans, and scissors at each table where the students will be working. If the students will be working at their desks, have the supplies ready for distribution.

Presentation:

- Have the students sit in a circle on the floor, legs crossed.
- Have the students take turns saying their name, age, grade, brothers' and sisters' names and ages, and their pets' names.
- Discuss how everyone is good at something, but no one is good at everything. Begin by saying, "Tiger Woods is an incredible golfer, but not an incredible basketball player." Continue by saying the names of other famous people and what they are famous for, then have the students finish the sentence with something they are not famous for.
- Begin with yourself. State something you are really good at, and then state something you need help with. Then have the students state something they are really good at and something they need help with and would need to practice a lot to do well.
- Discuss how sports, television, music, etc. would not be as interesting or exciting if everyone did everything the same way or at the same level. Tell the students to imagine how boring the Olympics would be if everyone had the same ability as everyone else.
- Have the students move to tables with pencils, paper, markers, crayons, construction paper, gluesticks or tape, scissors, cans, and stickers or to their desks. If the students will be working at their desks, distribute the supplies to each student.
- On the piece of paper, have each student write 20 things he/she can do really well, beginning each sentence with, "I can ...".

- Then have each student glue or tape construction paper so it covers the outside of the empty can and write on the front of the can, “My ‘I CAN’ Can.” The students may decorate their can with pictures of themselves doing things they do well or in any way they choose.

- Have the students cut the 20 things they wrote into 20 strips of paper and place the strips in the can.

- Have the students return to the circle. Explain that they may keep this can in their room at home and add another “I Can” strip every time they learn something new. Tell them that before they realize it, their cans will be overflowing.

- Continue by saying that if they feel sad or down about something, they can remove the strips from the can and remind themselves of all of their accomplishments.

- Ask the students to share their cans with the group. Then allow them to take the cans home.

SUGGESTED SELF-ESTEEM ACTIVITIES
GRADES 1-5

SELF-ESTEEM ACTIVITY #I:

Before presenting the activity, draw a sad/mean face and a happy face on posterboard, then cut the faces out. Hold up the happy face and tell the children it is a picture of Emily. Then say:

> *Emily feels really good about herself. You can say she has good or high self-esteem.* (Hold the picture high in the air.) *She feels like you may feel when you wake up on your birthday. She feels like she has lots of friends. She feels loved. She feels like she looks nice, and she knows she is a special person.*

Hold up the sad/mean face and tell the children it is a picture of Thomas. Then say:

> *Thomas has low or poor self-esteem.* (Hold the picture down low.) *He feels like no one likes him. He doesn't like how he looks. He feels sad and angry most of the time.*

Distribute paper and crayons or markers to each child. Have the children draw a happy face on one side of the paper and a sad face on the other. When everyone has finished, tell the students to write three things on the happy face that a person with high self-esteem might think and three things on the sad face that a person with low self-esteem might think. Have the children share their pictures.

SELF-ESTEEM ACTIVITY #2:

Show the happy face of Emily from the activity above and hold it up high. Tell the children:

> *When Emily wakes up, she feels great about herself. She walks to the bus feeling great.*

Show the children the sad/mean face of Thomas and hold the picture down low. Then continue:

> *When Emily gets on the bus, Thomas says something to hurt her feelings. When he says, "I hate your dress," Emily doesn't feel as happy.* (Lower the happy face.) *Throughout the day, Thomas continues to say mean things to Emily. Each time he does, she feels lower.* (Lower the happy face until it is lower than Thomas'.) *Thomas feels bad about himself and he wants Emily to feel as low as he does. Now it is up to Emily to choose how she feels.* (Raise the happy face up high again.)

Repeat each thing again that Thomas said to Emily, but this time, have Emily say, "Thank you very much" whenever he says something rude and hold her head high. Tell the children that they, like Emily, can choose to feel really low like Thomas or feel good about themselves, like Emily, and not let rude people change how they feel about themselves.

SELF-ESTEEM ACTIVITY #3:

Tell the children:

> *No matter where you are, you are special. You affect people at home with the great things you do. You affect people at school with the great things you do. You affect people in your community with the great things you do.*

Give each child a large piece of drawing paper and crayons or markers. Then give the following directions, pausing after each step, for the children to complete the instruction:

> *Fold your paper into thirds. On the top half of the first third, draw your house. On the top half of the second third, draw your school. On the top half of the last third draw your neighborhood.*

Allow the students time to complete their drawings, then say:

> *Below the drawing of your house write or draw three things you do at home that people think are great, like setting the table, giving hugs, or making others laugh. Now, below the drawing of your school, draw or write three things you do at school that people think are great, like sharing with others, listening well to the teacher, or helping the teacher. Finally, below the drawing of your neighborhood, write or draw three special things you do in your neighborhood, such as picking up trash, playing ball with younger kids, or helping someone rake leaves.*

When everyone has finished, have the students share their pictures and emphasize how special they are to so many people in so many places.

WHAT I THINK OTHERS WOULD SAY ABOUT ME

Name ________________________________ Date ______________

1. My best friend would say ______________________

   ____.

2. My teachers would say ______________________

   ____.

3. My brother/sister would say ______________________

   ____.

4. The counselor would say ______________________

   ____.

5. The person who sits next to me in class would say ___

   ____.

6. People in my neighborhood would say______________

   ____.

7. What I would say about myself is ________________

   ____.

Name ______________________________ Date ______________

20 THINGS I LIKE ABOUT ME

1. ______________________________
2. ______________________________
3. ______________________________
4. ______________________________
5. ______________________________
6. ______________________________
7. ______________________________
8. ______________________________
9. ______________________________
10. ______________________________
11. ______________________________
12. ______________________________
13. ______________________________
14. ______________________________
15. ______________________________
16. ______________________________
17. ______________________________
18. ______________________________
19. ______________________________
20. ______________________________

MOM'S HOMEWORK

Name ______________________________ **Date** ______________

Please write 20 things you like about me. Please put this paper in the envelope and **DO NOT SHOW IT TO ME!** Next week, we will read them in the counselor's office. Your list is a surprise!

20 THINGS YOU LIKE ABOUT ME

1. ______________________________
2. ______________________________
3. ______________________________
4. ______________________________
5. ______________________________
6. ______________________________
7. ______________________________
8. ______________________________
9. ______________________________
10. ______________________________
11. ______________________________
12. ______________________________
13. ______________________________
14. ______________________________
15. ______________________________
16. ______________________________
17. ______________________________
18. ______________________________
19. ______________________________
20. ______________________________

DAD'S HOMEWORK

Name ______________________________ **Date** ______________

Please write 20 things you like about me. Please put this paper in the envelope and **DO NOT SHOW IT TO ME!** Next week, we will read them in the counselor's office. Your list is a surprise!

20 THINGS YOU LIKE ABOUT ME

1. ______________________________
2. ______________________________
3. ______________________________
4. ______________________________
5. ______________________________
6. ______________________________
7. ______________________________
8. ______________________________
9. ______________________________
10. ______________________________
11. ______________________________
12. ______________________________
13. ______________________________
14. ______________________________
15. ______________________________
16. ______________________________
17. ______________________________
18. ______________________________
19. ______________________________
20. ______________________________

SELF-ESTEEM REMOTE CONTROL

YOU CONTROL HOW YOU FEEL ABOUT YOURSELF

Turn on positive thoughts.
On

Turn off negative thoughts.
Off

Speak up about yourself, not down.
Volume

If you start feeling bad about yourself, change the channel and think of great things you have done.
Channel

Stop thinking you are bad or a loser if you make a mistake or lose a game.
Stop

Play well with others and you will feel good about yourself.
Play

Count all of the wonderful things you are good at.

12345....

There is no *Rewind* button on the Self-Esteem Remote Control. You cannot go back and say something or do something again.

DON'T WORRY ABOUT THE PAST. JUST LEARN FROM YOUR MISTAKES!

Everyone is
good at
SOMETHING,
but no one is
good at
EVERYTHING!

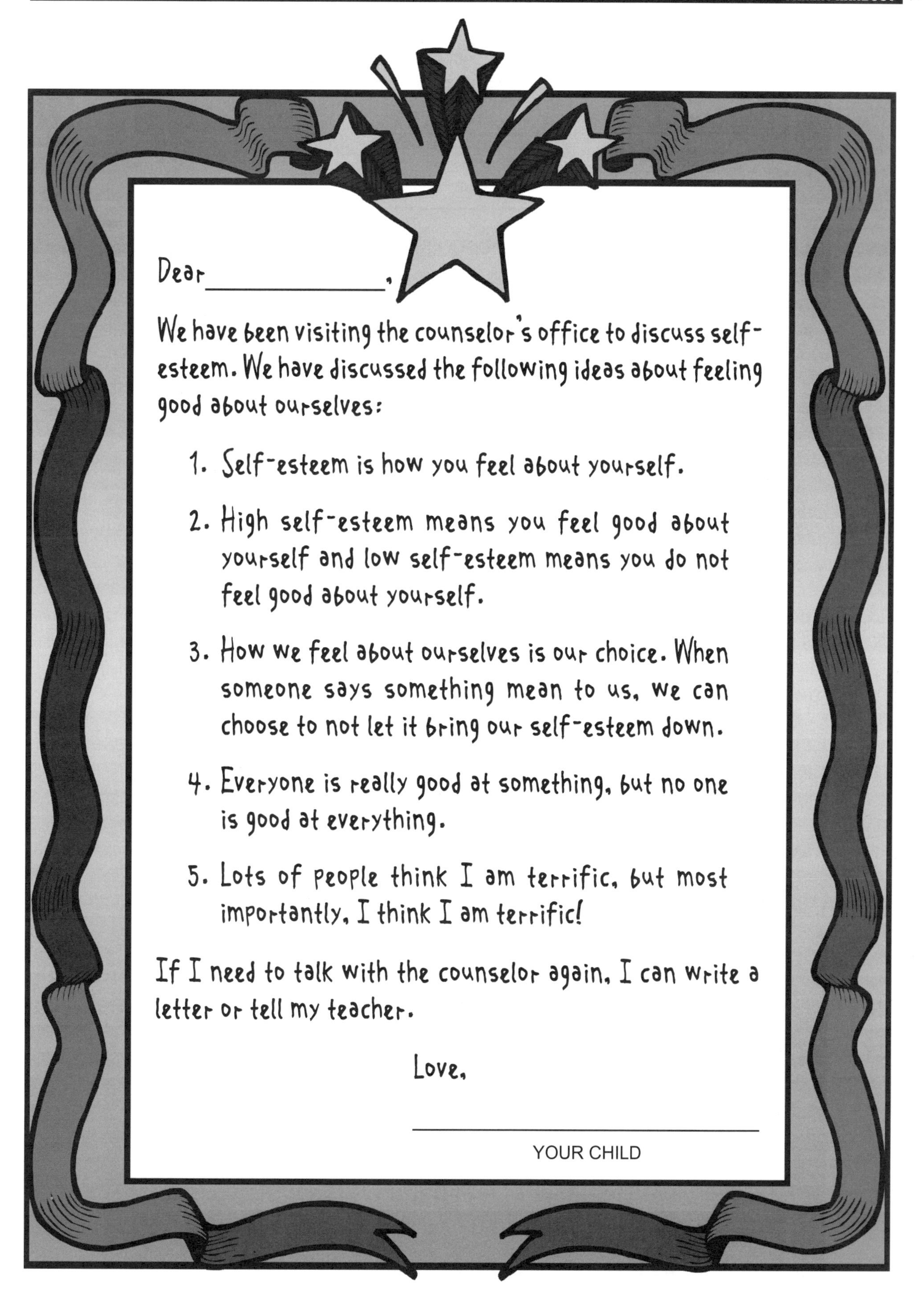

Dear_______________,

We have been visiting the counselor's office to discuss self-esteem. We have discussed the following ideas about feeling good about ourselves:

1. Self-esteem is how you feel about yourself.
2. High self-esteem means you feel good about yourself and low self-esteem means you do not feel good about yourself.
3. How we feel about ourselves is our choice. When someone says something mean to us, we can choose to not let it bring our self-esteem down.
4. Everyone is really good at something, but no one is good at everything.
5. Lots of people think I am terrific, but most importantly, I think I am terrific!

If I need to talk with the counselor again, I can write a letter or tell my teacher.

Love,

____

YOUR CHILD

SELF-ESTEEM GROUP STUDENT EVALUATION

NAME ______________________________ **DATE** __________

TEACHER ______________________________

Please answer the following questions about the Self-Esteem Group **HONESTLY**:

1. I enjoyed coming to the counselor's office. (Please circle one.)

   A LOT **A LITTLE** **NOT AT ALL**

2. I learned things in this group that I didn't already know. (Please circle one.)

   A LOT **A LITTLE** **NOT AT ALL**

3. The thing I liked best about this group was:

   ____

   ____

4. The thing I didn't like about this group was:

   ____

   ____

5. Three (3) things I learned in this group were:

   A. ______________________________

   ____

   B. ______________________________

   ____

   C. ______________________________

   ____

6. I would like to be a member of another group with the counselor. (Please circle one.)

   A LOT **A LITTLE** **NOT AT ALL**

FRIENDSHIP

SMALL-GROUP COUNSELING
CLASSROOM GUIDANCE

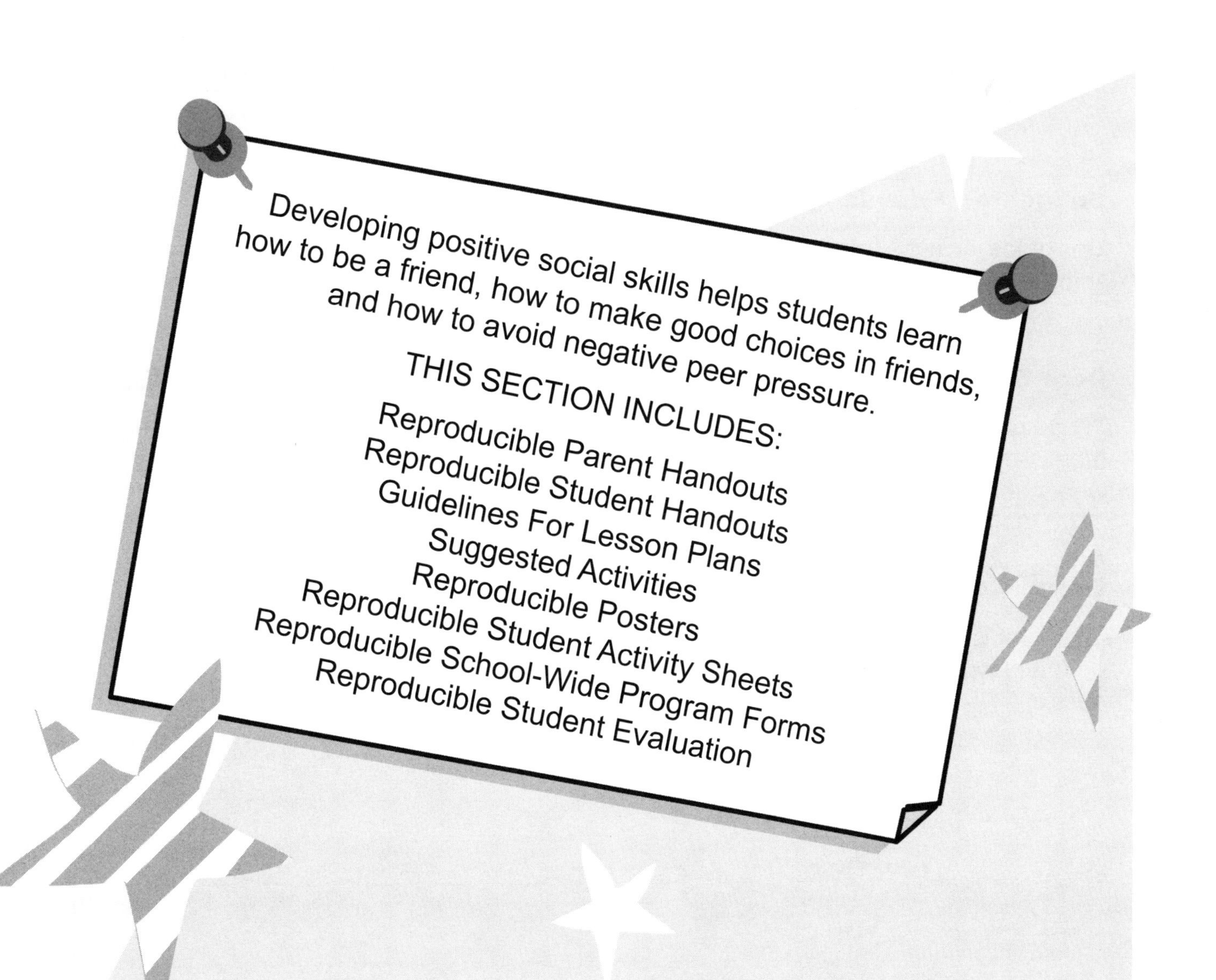

Friendship Group Parent Permission Form (page 122) **SG PH**

Distribute this sheet to parents of all children in the targeted grade levels.

Student Evaluation Form (page 123) **TH**

This form, given to teachers prior to the first session, provides an opportunity for them to tell the counselor which friendship behaviors need to be addressed with the student.

Friendship Lesson Plan Grades K-2 (pages 124-127) **SG CG**

This guideline for presenting material to grades K-2 includes a step-by-step guide for presentation, discussion, and interactive activities. Also included is the reproducible *Empathy Activity* sheet and the reproducible *Empathy* poster.

Friendship Lesson Plan Grades 3-5 (pages 128-130) **SG CG**

This guideline for presenting material to grades 3-5 includes a step-by-step guide for presentation, discussion, and interactive activities. Also included is the reproducible *Friendship* activity sheet and the *Share Your Friends, You Do Not Own Them!* poster.

Suggested Friendship Activities Grades 1-5 (page 131) **SG SA**

This guide includes three suggested activities for use with students participating in the Friendship Group.

Dear Friend Letter (pages 132-133) **IND SG CG SH**

These pages are given to students during individual counseling or classroom guidance or to members of a Friendship Group. These letters will help students learn exactly what to do and what not to do to make and keep friends. The letter should be signed by the counselor.

Group Cooperation Evaluation (page 134) **SW SH**

This form is to be used by groups of friends who have difficulty getting along with each other on the playground. The counselor may want to review and discuss the forms after each recess.

Ideas For Friendship Practice (pages 135-136) **IND SG CG PH**

Students should take home these pages and ask their parents to help them practice the friendship skills learned during the sessions with the counselor. This activity helps parents become involved in reinforcing these new skills at home.

Classroom Friendship Plan (page 137) **SW PH**

This parent letter can be used when members of a group of girls do not get along and several adult interventions have not proven effective. This plan requires the principal and the counselor to closely monitor the situation. The letter also suggests ways for parents to deal with friendship issues at home.

Post Friendship Small-Group Counseling Letter For Parents (page 138) **SG PH**

Sending letters to parents at the end of small-group counseling sessions is courteous and appreciated.

Friendship Group Student Evaluation (page 139) **SG SH**

Feedback from students is an invaluable resource that helps counselors plan for future group sessions. Distribute the evaluation sheet at the final group meeting.

Dear Parents:

I will be initiating FRIENDSHIP small-group counseling sessions in the next month. During these sessions, we will discuss specific behaviors that may keep students from getting along with their friends and ways to replace those behaviors with appropriate ones. In addition, we will discuss different types of friends and how to get along with each type.

These sessions will meet once a week for ________ weeks. The ___-minute group may not be held on consecutive weeks, due to field trips, assemblies, holidays, etc.

If you feel your child's friendship issues are interfering with his/her academics, please sign the following permission form and return it to your child's teacher by ____________________________. The first group session will begin as soon as an appropriate schedule is worked out with your child's classroom teacher.

I would like to help you and your child make the rest of the school year as successful as possible. If you would like to discuss your child, or you have any questions or concerns, please do not hesitate to contact me.

Sincerely,

____

WE CARE ABOUT KIDS

- -

I, ____________________________________, give permission for my child to participate in the FRIENDSHIP GROUP with the counselor.

Child's Name ____________________________________ Date ___________

School ____ Grade _________

Teacher _______________________________________

Home Phone (_______) ___________________________

Work Phone (_______) ___________________________

Parent's Printed Name ____________________________

Parent's Signature _______________________________

STUDENT EVALUATION FORM

Dear Teachers:

Please check the items below that are causing the most difficulty for ____________________________ .
I understand this student is having problems making and/or keeping friends and I'd like to help.

Thank you,

____

- ☐ Is bossy
- ☐ Is easily influenced by the remarks of other students
- ☐ Is a "follower"
- ☐ Tattles frequently
- ☐ Has difficulty relating to the other students
- ☐ Does not have many "true" friends
- ☐ Constantly tries to please both adults and peers
- ☐ Is often a loner
- ☐ Tries to "buy" friendships with material gifts or promises
- ☐ Waits to be asked to join games or groups
- ☐ Tries to impress others and, consequently, drives them away
- ☐ Uses gossip as a technique to win friends

FRIENDSHIP LESSON PLAN

GRADES K-2

Materials Needed:

- ☐ Chalkboard and chalk or dry-erase board and marker
- ☐ Copy of *Empathy Activity* (page 126) for each student
- ☐ Copy of *Empathy* (page 127) for each student
- ☐ Red and green crayon for each student

Pre-Presentation Preparation:

Write the word *Empathy* on the board. Reproduce *Empathy Activity* and *Empathy* for each student.

Presentation:

- Have the students sit in a circle on the floor, legs crossed.
- Have each student take turns saying his/her name and the name of his/her favorite vegetable.
- Tell the children:

  You are going to learn a grown-up word. (Point to the word *Empathy* on the board.) *This word is so important that if you do what this word means every day, you will have lots of friends for the rest of your lives.*

  The word is empathy *and it means* to think about how the other person feels before you say something or do something.

- Tell the children that, if they choose to do so, they may take off their shoes and put them in front of where they are sitting. The leader should do the same. Then say:

  Empathy means pretending to be in someone else's shoes before you say or do something. You have to stop and think about whether what you are going to say or do will hurt someone's feelings.

- Ask for a volunteer to come to the center of the circle and stand in front of the leader. Then say:

    We are going to pretend that this student is about to say to me, "I don't like your shirt/dress." But before he/she says this, I want him/her to stand in my shoes and pretend to be me.

- After the volunteer is standing in your shoes, ask:

    How do you think I will feel when you tell me you don't like my shirt/dress? (The volunteers answer will be bad, mad, sad, and any other appropriate answer.)

- Have the volunteer step out of your shoes and say whether he/she is going to tell you that he/she doesn't like your shirt/dress. (The volunteer should say that he/she is NOT going to say it because he/she doesn't want to hurt your feelings.)

- Upon hearing this, have the students applaud.

- Ask for another volunteer. Tell the student to pretend he/she is about to say, "I sure like your new haircut." Have the volunteer stop and think, then step into your shoes and repeat the process the previous volunteer completed.

- Ask for two volunteers. Tell each volunteer to think of a positive statement and a negative statement. Then have each stand in the other's shoes and practice the process of stopping, thinking, and deciding if what they are going to say will hurt the other person's feelings.

- Continue this activity until every student has had a chance to participate.

- Distribute *Empathy Activity* and a red and green crayon to each child. Review the directions. Then either complete the activity sheet as a group or, if the students are capable of understanding the directions and reading the words, have them complete it on their own.

- When everyone has finished, review the answers if the children completed the activity sheet on their own.

- Distribute the *Empathy* poster. Read the poster aloud with the children. Allow the children to take both papers home.

EMPATHY ACTIVITY

Directions: Read what each boy or girl is about to say. Stop. Think. Pretend you are that person. Decide whether the statement will hurt someone's feelings. If the statement WILL NOT hurt someone's feelings, color the happy circle GREEN. If the statement WILL hurt someone's feelings, color the sad circle RED.

1. You don't have any friends.

2. I want to play with you.

3. I think you did a great job.

4. I don't like your hair.

5. Yuck! What are you eating for lunch?

6. I don't want to play with you.

7. I was here first and you are in my way.

8. You can play on the swings with us.

9. My sister doesn't like you very much.

10. Here, let me share with you.

11. You can't come to my party.

12. Your dog looks really dirty.

13. I want to help you.

14. Get away from me!

EMPATHY

Think about how someone else feels
before saying something
or doing something.

Pretend you are the other
person and put yourself
"in his/her shoes."

The word PATH is
in emPATHy
because empathy is the
path to friendship.

FRIENDSHIP LESSON PLAN
GRADES 3-5

Materials Needed:

- ☐ Chalkboard and chalk or dry-erase board and marker
- ☐ Copy of *Friendship* (page 129) for each student
- ☐ Copy of *Share Your Friends* (page 130) for each student
- ☐ Piece of plain paper and pencil for each student

Pre-Presentation Preparation:

Write the word *Friend* on the board. Reproduce *Friendship* and *Share Your Friends* for each student.

Presentation:

- Have the students sit in a circle on the floor, legs crossed.
- Have each student take turns saying his/her name and the name of his/her favorite movie.
- Ask the children the meaning of the word *friend* and write all of their definitions on the board.
- Tell the students:

  I am going to give each of you an activity sheet that will require you to be TOTALLY HONEST with yourselves. I will also give each of you a piece of paper to cover your answers in order to keep them private.

- Distribute *Friendship*, a pencil, and a piece of plain paper to each student. Review the directions and have the students complete the activity sheet.
- When the students have completed the activity sheet, say:

  Look at what you have circled under How To Lose Friends. *Choose one item to improve upon each week. In other words, if you have circled five things, choose to improve upon one a week for five weeks.*

- Distribute *Share Your Friends* to each student. Encourage the students to hang the poster in a place at school or home where its message can easily remind them of a way to make and keep friends.

FRIENDSHIP

Directions: Be **TOTALLY HONEST** with yourself! Circle the following things that you do to make friends and the things that you may do that cause you to lose friends.

- Smile a lot
- Give them compliments
- Be dependable
- Share your things
- Share your friends—let them play with others
- Look in a person's eyes when he or she is talking
- Before you say something or do something, think about how the other person will feel
- Let them play with you
- Be honest
- Listen to them
- Use a friendly voice

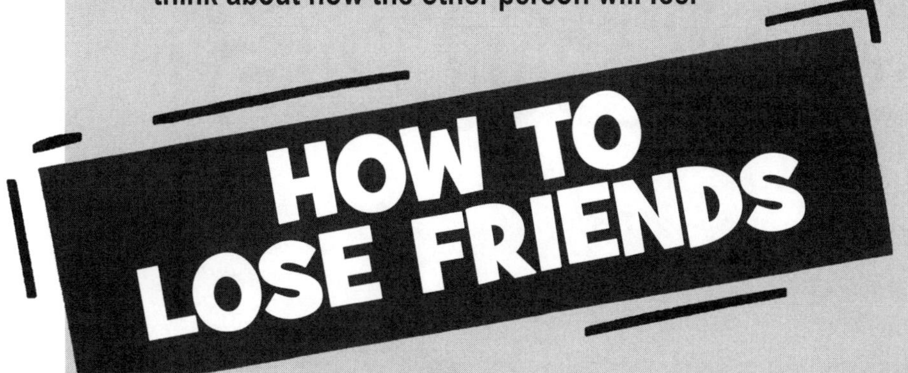

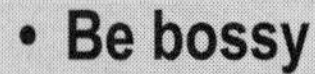

- Be bossy
- Say mean things to them
- Say things without thinking
- Brag about yourself
- Tell your friends' secrets to others
- Joke about them to get others to laugh
- Make sure things always have to be your way
- Tell your friends they may play only with you
- Stop being their friend every time you have an argument
- Don't stand up for them if someone teases or bullies them
- Get mad if they want to play with someone else sometimes
- Tell them you won't be their friend if they don't do what you want them to do
- Show off to get attention
- Argue with them a lot
- Talk behind their back

Share
your
Friends!
you Do not
OWN
them!

SUGGESTED FRIENDSHIP ACTIVITIES
GRADES 1-5

FRIENDSHIP ACTIVITY #I:

Ask the children to tell the meaning of the word *shy*. Then say:

> *Being shy is not a bad thing. A shy person can be a very good listener. Another good thing about being shy is that shy people usually stop and think before saying or doing things.*

Play a game of *Build A Man*. Write the following blanks on the board:

____ ____ ____ ____ ____   ____ ____ ____

____ ____   ____ ____

Have the children guess which letter belongs in each of the blanks. If they do not guess a letter correctly, draw a head, then a body, then 2 arms and 2 legs. If they guess the message before you complete the man, they win. The message is: *Being shy is OK.*

FRIENDSHIP ACTIVITY #2:

Tell the children that some people are shy about making new friends and ask the children to give examples of times they felt comfortable talking with others and times they felt uncomfortable. Have the children role-play ways to approach others on the playground by practicing asking, "May I play?" or "May I play the winner?" Have them also practice finding something to talk about with each other, such as, "I like the cars on your shirt. Do you like cars?" Then have the children discuss what they will do during the next week to approach another student.

FRIENDSHIP ACTIVITY #3:

Discuss the fact that some people are nervous about approaching others. This could be because they do not feel very good about themselves. Remind the children that everyone is special and then have each group member tell why he/she would be a good person to play with.

Distribute art paper and crayons or markers and have each of the children draw a picture of four things he/she can do really well. When everyone has finished, discuss the pictures and remind the students how lucky other children will be to play with them.

Dear Friend,

Making and keeping friends takes lots and lots of practice. Everyone wants to have more friends, so here is a list of things you can do to make and keep friends.

HOW TO MAKE FRIENDS:

1. Smile a lot.
2. Look people in their eyes when they are talking.
3. Use a friendly voice.
4. Use an inside voice.
5. Join games and let others join, too. Use some of these words:

"May I play, too?"
"When you have finished this game, may I play, too?"
"What would you like to play?"
"I'll share with you."
"Would you like a turn?"
"Congratulations on winning!"

6. Say nice things to other people about how well they did something or how nice they look. Use some of these words:

"I like your haircut."
"You did a great job on the spelling test."
"You are really good at playing basketball. Good shot!"
"I like your shoes. They are really cool."
"I like you because you always play fair."

7. Treat other people just like you want them to treat you!

Once you make friends, you have to work very hard to keep them. Here is a list of things to do to keep your friends.

over➡

HOW TO KEEP YOUR FRIENDS:

1. Smile a lot.
2. Say only nice things about your friends. Never say mean things to them.
3. All friends argue once in a while. Don't stop being someone's friend just because you disagree about something.
4. Never say mean things about your friend to others because what you say will always get back to your friend.
5. Let your friend have other friends. You do not *own* your friends. You *share* your friends.
6. Tell your friend that even if you argue, you still like him/her.
7. Don't ever tell other people whom to play with. That is their business, not yours.
8. Take turns picking a game and take turns going first.
9. Don't ever boss your friends around. You wouldn't want them to do that to you.
10. TREAT OTHER PEOPLE JUST LIKE YOU WANT THEM TO TREAT YOU!

I hope these ideas will help you make new friends and keep the friends you have. You may have to do these things for weeks and weeks before you have lots of friends, but never, ever give up! It is so wonderful that you came to someone to ask for help with making and keeping friends! Asking for help always helps you solve your problems more quickly and easily.

Take this paper home and ask an adult to help you practice these friendship tricks. GOOD LUCK!

I certainly am glad you are my friend.

____

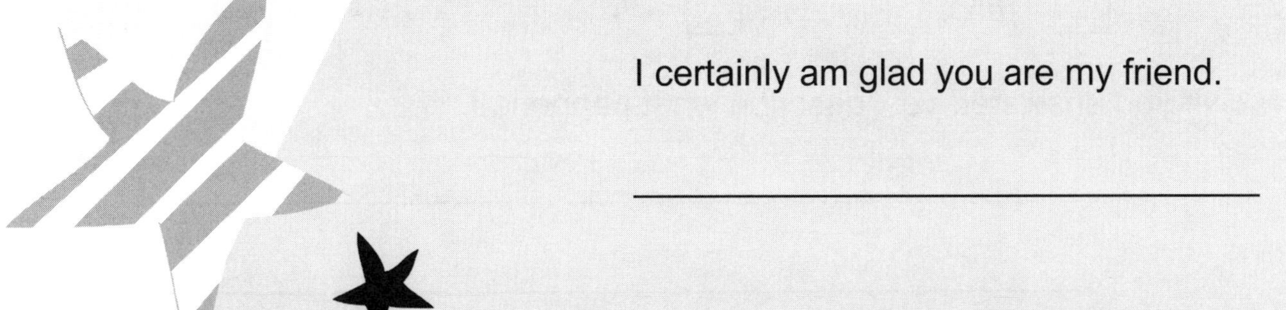

NAME ____________________ DATE __________

GROUP COOPERATION EVALUATION

1. On a scale of 1 to 10 (with 10 being the most cooperative), I would say we rated a _________ today.

2. The thing we did best was that we:

   ☐ A. Listened to each other
   ☐ B. Used compliments
   ☐ C. Let everyone participate in everything we did

3. The thing we will need to work on next time is:

   ☐ A. Listening to each other more
   ☐ B. Using compliments more
   ☐ C. Letting everyone participate in everything we do

4. Some compliments we used were:

   A. ______________________________
   B. ______________________________
   C. ______________________________

5. Did someone try to hurt your feelings?

   ☐ Yes ☐ No

   If you answered *yes*, describe what happened.

   ____
   ____
   ____

Dear ______________________________,

Please practice these *Conversation Starters* with me this week so I can demonstrate them for the counselor at our next session on _____________.

Thank you,

____

Talk about the weather outside ...

"It sure is cold!"

Say something nice ...

"I like your new shirt."

Ask someone to play a game ...

"Would you like to play checkers with me?"

Dear ________________________,

We came up with these ways to make new friends.

Please practice these with me so I can demonstrate them for the counselor at our next meeting on _____________________.

1. Ask someone if he/she wants to play.
2. Ask others questions about themselves.
3. Talk about the weather.
4. Give someone a compliment.
5. Talk about sports.
6. Help someone with something.
7. Let someone play a game with you.
8. Talk about birthdays.
9. Ask someone to go somewhere with you.
10. Tell someone what you did over the weekend, then ask that person what he/she did.

Dear Parents,

The principal and I are aware of some concerns regarding the relationships between several girls in ______________________________'s classroom. Most of these issues stem from the girls not showing respect for each other.

Relationship issues are very common at this grade level and at this time of the school year. However, we make it clear to all students that no one has the right to treat others badly. When these issues arise at school, we follow a specific plan of action. If the first step does not work, we proceed to the second and, as a last resort, go to the third step. The plan is as follows:

1. Students meet with me to discuss various strategies for handling problems when they arise.
2. Students make a Friendship Folder that allows them to monitor themselves each day so they can evaluate how they handled their own problem. They earn stickers for accomplished behaviors. When they earn a specific number of stickers, they are invited to have a pizza lunch in my office.
3. The students in conflict play only with each other for three days and use the strategies they have learned to work on solving their friendship problems. After recess each of those days, they are required to come to my office or to the principal's office to report on their progress.

There are several strategies you may find helpful to practice with your child to help her make and keep friends. The following suggestions will help you teach your child to handle situations independently.

1. When your child arrives home, ask her to spend several minutes writing in a journal a positive and a negative thing that happened at school that day. Later that evening, spend 20 minutes discussing the day's journal entry with your child. When that time is up, move on to another activity.

   This strategy helps alleviate negative comments after school. The more you listen to negativity, and the more you react to it, the less positive your child will be. Her negative comments could go on endlessly.
2. Role-play specific friendship problems with your child. You can pretend to be your child and she can pretend to be the other child. Act out the problem, then act out what your child can do to solve the problem.

   This strategy helps children see the steps necessary for managing a conflict.
3. Invite your child's friends to your house to write, act out, and practice conflict-management skills. Sit back and see how your child handles each situation.

   This can help you see what areas your child needs to work on when her friends leave.
4. Watch television programs with your child. Point out positive or negative friendship issues, and discuss one.

   Many sitcoms, and even cartoons, include some type of relationship issue to be solved. These are perfect opportunities to engage your child in conversations about appropriate and inappropriate methods of conflict management.

In the past, the strategies above have proven beneficial in dealing with conflicts. We hope they will be helpful to you and your child.

Sincerely,

Dear Parents:

Your child has been coming to my office to discuss friendship. We have discussed the following aspects of being a good friend.

1. **Empathy is the path to friendship.**
2. **Our words and actions affect others.**
3. **Things others do that may "bug" us.**
4. **Things we do that may "bug" others.**
5. **Bossiness does not make friends.**
6. **The more friends you have who behave in a positive way, the better.**
7. **Don't tell others they cannot be someone else's friend.**
8. **Compromise.**

In our group, we have practiced friendship skills, being polite, and being kind to one another.

After this group concludes, the children know they can visit with me by writing a letter or telling their teacher they want to speak with me. If I can help you or your child again, please let me know.

Sincerely,

FRIENDSHIP GROUP STUDENT EVALUATION

NAME ______________________________ DATE ____________

TEACHER ______________________________

Please answer the following questions about the Friendship Group **HONESTLY**:

1. I enjoyed coming to the counselor's office. (Please circle one.)

   A LOT **A LITTLE** **NOT AT ALL**

2. I learned things in this group that I didn't already know. (Please circle one.)

   A LOT **A LITTLE** **NOT AT ALL**

3. The thing I liked best about this group was:

   ____

   ____

4. The thing I didn't like about this group was:

   ____

   ____

5. Three (3) things I learned in this group were:

   A. ____

   ____

   B. ____

   ____

   C. ____

   ____

6. I would like to be a member of another group with the counselor. (Please circle one.)

   A LOT **A LITTLE** **NOT AT ALL**

Anger Management

SMALL-GROUP COUNSELING
CLASSROOM GUIDANCE

Anger is a primary emotion that affects everyone. When we do not have the ability to control it, anger leads to destructive behaviors and destructive relationships. Use these forms and lessons to help children learn that being angry is okay and how to react to anger in positive ways.

THIS SECTION INCLUDES:

Reproducible Parent Handouts
Guidelines For Lesson Plans
Suggested Activities
Reproducible Posters
Reproducible Student Activity Sheets
Reproducible Student Evaluation Sheet

Anger-Management Group Parent Permission Form (page 143) **SG PH**

Distribute this sheet to parents of all children in the targeted grade levels.

Student Evaluation Form (page 144) **TH**

This form, given to teachers prior to the first session, provides an opportunity for them to tell the counselor which anger-management behaviors need to be addressed with the student.

Anger-Management
Lesson Plan Grades K-2 (pages 145-148) **SG CG**

This guideline for presenting material to grades K-2 includes a step-by-step guide for presentation, discussion, and interactive activities. Also included is the reproducible *Anger Busters* activity sheet and the reproducible *Anger Rules* poster.

Anger-Management
Lesson Plan Grades 3-5 (pages 149-150) **SG CG**

This guideline for presenting material to grades 3-5 includes a step-by-step guide for presentation, discussion, and interactive activities. Also included is the reproducible *Anger Rules* poster.

Suggested Anger-Management
Activities Grades 1-5 (page 151) **SG SA**

This includes three suggested activities for use with students participating in the Anger-Management Group.

Post Anger-Management Small-Group Counseling
Letters For Parents (pages 152-153) **SG PH**

Sending letters to parents at the end of small-group counseling sessions is courteous and appreciated.

Anger-Management Group Student Evaluation (page 154) **SG SH**

Feedback from students is an invaluable resource that helps counselors plan for future group sessions. Distribute the evaluation sheet at the final group meeting.

Dear Parents:

I will be initiating ANGER-MANAGEMENT small-group counseling sessions in the next month. During these sessions, we will discuss the reasons we get angry and the consequences of acting out those feelings inappropriately. Participants will learn appropriate anger expression and that angry feelings are perfectly okay, as long as they are dealt with without hurting others, without hurting oneself, and without damaging property.

These sessions will meet once a week for ________ weeks. The ___-minute group may not be held on consecutive weeks, due to field trips, assemblies, holidays, etc.

If you feel your child's anger issues are interfering with his/her academics, please sign the following permission form and return it to your child's teacher by ____________________________. The first group session will begin as soon as an appropriate schedule is worked out with your child's classroom teacher.

I would like to help you and your child make the rest of the school year as successful as possible. If you would like to discuss your child, or you have any questions or concerns, please do not hesitate to contact me.

Sincerely,

____

WE CARE ABOUT KIDS

I, ___________________________________, give permission for my child to participate in the ANGER-MANAGEMENT GROUP with the counselor.

Child's Name ___________________________________ Date __________

School ____ Grade _________

Teacher _______________________________________

Home Phone (_______) __________________________

Work Phone (_______) __________________________

Parent's Printed Name ___________________________

Parent's Signature ______________________________

STUDENT EVALUATION FORM

Dear Teachers:

Please check the items below that are causing the most difficulty for ________________________ .
I understand this student needs help with anger management.

Thank you,

____

- ☐ Loses temper easily
- ☐ Displays anger when receiving a poor grade
- ☐ When angry, calls other students names
- ☐ Physically fights with students
- ☐ Destroys things when angry
- ☐ Goes into "withdrawal" when angry
- ☐ Is frequently in a bad or angry mood
- ☐ Has home problems which affect his/her anger in school
- ☐ Deals with anger by crying, whining, and/or pouting
- ☐ Poor sportsmanship
- ☐ Wants his/her own way in games or group projects
- ☐ Threatens other students

ANGER-MANAGEMENT LESSON PLAN
GRADES K-2

Materials Needed:

- ☐ Balloon (not inflated)
- ☐ Straight pin or safety pin
- ☐ Pillow
- ☐ Tissues and trash can
- ☐ Clay
- ☐ Blank piece of paper for each student
- ☐ Pencil and crayons for each student
- ☐ Copy of *Anger Rules* (page 147) for each student
- ☐ Copy of *Anger Busters* (page 148) for each student
- ☐ Sticker for each student

Pre-Presentation Preparation:

Reproduce a copy of *Anger Rules* and *Anger Busters* for each student. Make sure the pin is hidden, but that you can discretely pick it up when you need it during the lesson.

Presentation:

- Have the students sit in a circle on the floor, legs crossed.

- Have the students take turns saying their names, one thing that makes them happy, and one thing that makes them angry.

- Tell the children:

  It is okay to be angry. Everyone gets angry. When you are angry, your body fills up with angry energy.

  How does your body feel when you are angry? (Pause for responses.)

- While blowing up the balloon, discretely put the pin in your other hand. Continue by saying:

  I am going to tell you a story about a little boy who wanted to play on the swings at school, but they were all taken. This made him angry. (Blow up the balloon a little.) *The little boy asked another boy to share the swings with him, but the other boy said, "No." This made the little boy angrier.* (Blow the balloon up a little more.)

- Continue to talk about the little boy and what made him angry until the balloon is completely blown up. Using the pin, pop the balloon. Then say:

  Children who lose their tempers scare others when they explode, just like the popping of the balloon can scare you. Others do not want to be around these children, because they are afraid they will explode at any minute.

  It is okay to get angry. Everyone gets angry. But when you are angry, you should never break the Anger Rules.

- Distribute *Anger Rules* to each child and review what is written on the poster.

- Give the children examples of *Anger Busters*—things they can do to get rid of their angry energy without breaking the *Anger Rules*, like screaming into a pillow, tearing up a tissue into little pieces and throwing it in a trash can, scribbling on paper, pounding on clay, running in place, counting to 20, etc. Give each child a piece of paper and a pencil. Then have the children practice each of the things you have suggested.

- Distribute *Anger Busters* and crayons to each child. Review the directions, then have the children complete the sheet by drawing themselves getting rid of their angry energy in each box.

- When everyone has finished, have the students share one of their drawings with the group. Put a sticker on each paper and send the paper home for the children to practice with their parents what they have learned.

- Encourage them to display *Anger Rules* at home or at school in a place where it will easily remind them of its message.

ANGER RULES
It is perfectly OK to get angry, but...
Do not hurt others' bodies or feelings.
Do not destroy property.
Do not hurt yourself.

ANGER BUSTERS

In each box, draw a picture of yourself getting rid of your angry energy.

When I am angry, these are the things I can do to get rid of my angry energy ...

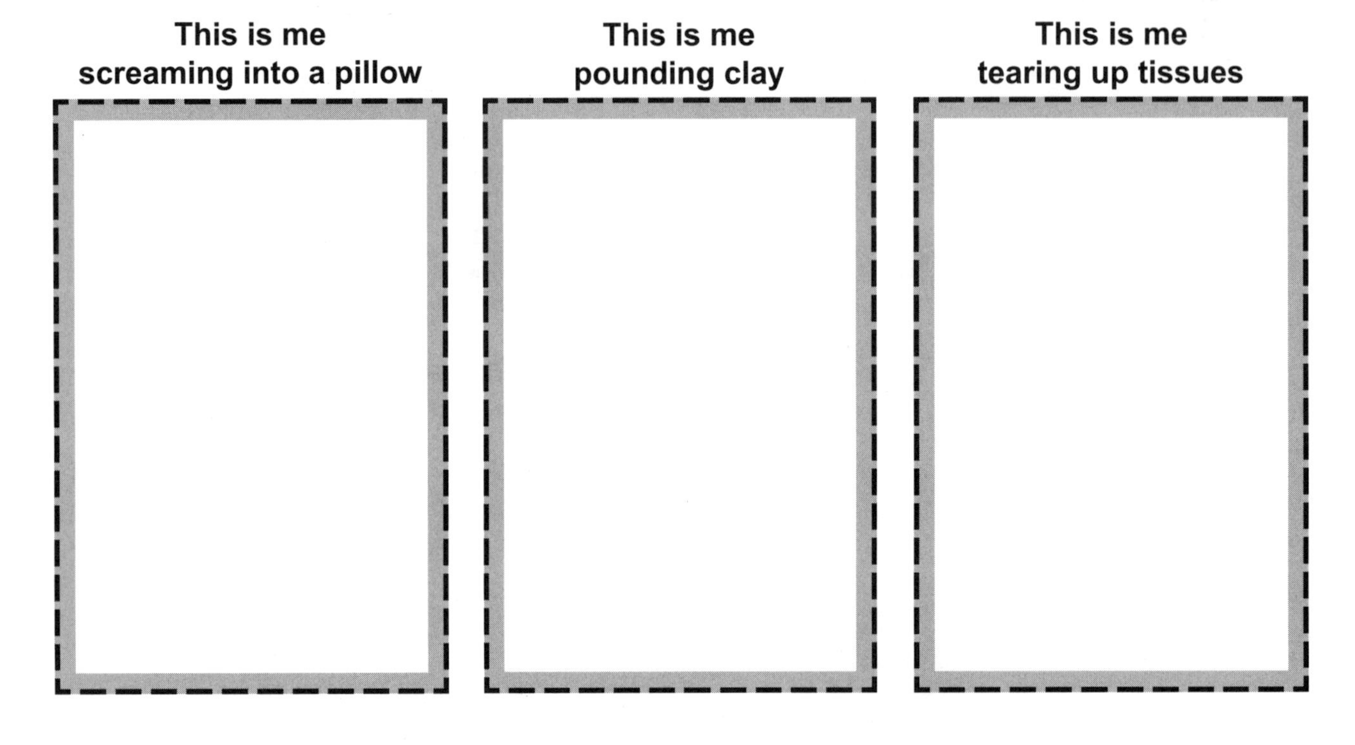

This is me screaming into a pillow

This is me pounding clay

This is me tearing up tissues

This is me scribbling on paper

This is me counting to 20

This is me running in place

ANGER MANAGEMENT LESSON PLAN
GRADES 3-5

Materials Needed:

- ☐ Copy of *Anger Rules* (page 147)
- ☐ Drawing paper for each student
- ☐ Pencil, markers, and crayons for each student
- ☐ Stickers for each student

Pre-Presentation Preparation:

Display the *Anger Rules* poster in a place in the room where all the children can easily see it.

Presentation:

- Have the students sit in a circle on the floor, legs crossed.
- Have the students take turns saying their names, one thing that makes them happy, and one thing that makes them angry.
- Tell the children:

    It is okay to be angry. Everyone gets angry. When you are angry, your body fills up with angry energy.

    How does your body feel when you are angry? (Pause for responses.)

- Show the children the *Anger Rules* poster and tell them they must always follow these rules when they are angry.
- Choose three volunteers. Have each volunteer read one rule and state why he/she thinks it is important.
- Without using any names, have the students tell of times they have seen someone break an *Anger Rule.*

- Divide the students into groups of three. Then explain:

  Your group is to make up a skit. Each member of your group is responsible for acting out the rule that corresponds with the number he/she has been assigned and the number on the Anger Rules poster in that skit. For example, each group will make up a skit in which the players pretend they are angry about something. Member #1 will handle his/her anger by pretending to hurt someone's body or feelings, member #2 will handle his/her anger by pretending to break something, and member #3 will pretend to hurt him/herself.

  Be sure the students understand they are only to *pretend* to hurt someone or to break something. Then say:

  Without letting anyone else in the room hear what you are planning, assign each member of your group a number and plan your skit. You will have about five minutes to do this.

- Have the children begin working on their skits. After the allotted time has elapsed, call *time* and have each group perform its skit. After each skit has been presented, the audience will guess which *Anger Rule* each member broke.

- Distribute drawing paper, crayons, pencils, markers, and stickers to each child. Ask them to make a colorful poster for their bedroom that states the *Anger Rules.*

- When everyone has finished, have the students share their posters with the group. They may take their posters home.

SUGGESTED ANGER-MANAGEMENT ACTIVITIES
GRADES 1-5

ANGER-MANAGEMENT ACTIVITY #I:

This activity is performed step-by-step as a group. Distribute drawing paper and crayons or markers to each student and, pausing after each direction, say:

> *You are to draw four faces of yourselves. First I want you to draw your face BEFORE you get angry. Next, draw your face WHEN you are angry. Now, draw your face AFTER you have been angry, like after you have hurt someone's feelings or body, broken something, or hurt yourselves.*

When everyone has finished, discuss how each face looks and how each face feels. Then have the students draw their faces AFTER they have handled their anger appropriately.

ANGER-MANAGEMENT ACTIVITY #2:

Distribute drawing paper and crayons or markers to each student. Then say:

> *Today you are going to draw your bodies. First, draw what the following parts of your body might look like when you are angry. Draw your eyes, teeth and mouth, hands, and tummy.*

Then have the students tell how each of those body parts feels when it is angry. Continue by discussing how the students feel as they begin to get angry and how it is important to begin to get rid of angry energy appropriately BEFORE anger gets out of control.

ANGER-MANAGEMENT ACTIVITY #3:

Tell the students they are going to "teach" the kindergarten or pre-school children how to treat others nicely. Have them tell the group what they think the younger students should know about treating each other with kindness. Then divide the students into groups and have each group write and practice role-playing situations that may occur on the playground and in the classroom. When all the role-plays have been presented, have the students perform them as skits for the younger students.

ANGER RULES

Dear _______________________________________,

In the counselor's office, I learned _________________________________

____

____

It is perfectly okay to get angry, but …

1. Do not hurt others' bodies or feelings.

2. Do not destroy property.

3. Do not hurt yourself.

Signed ____

Dear ________________________________ ,

I have been visiting the counselor's office to discuss anger. I have learned the following things:

1. It is perfectly okay to be angry.

2. When I get angry, my body fills with "angry energy." I need to get rid of that "angry energy." There are appropriate and inappropriate ways to do this.

3. I can get rid of "angry energy" appropriately if I follow three anger rules. These rules are:

    - Do not hurt others' bodies or feelings.
    - Do not destroy property.
    - Do not hurt yourself.

4. There are many things I can do to get rid of my "angry energy" while following these rules. These things are called *Anger Busters*. Some of them are:

    - Talk it out.
    - Count to 20.
    - Walk away.
    - Kick a ball outside.
    - Scream into a pillow.
    - Punch a pillow or punching bag.
    - Listen to music.
    - Tear a tissue into little pieces, then throw the pieces away.
    - Scribble on scratch paper.
    - Pound clay.
    - Exercise.

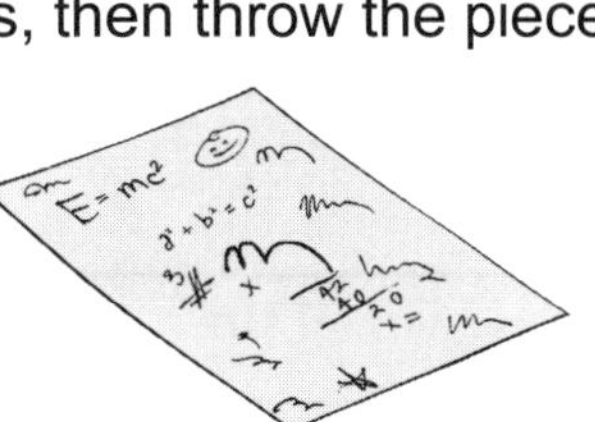

There are many more, but these are the *Anger Busters* we have discussed in most detail.

Please talk with me about the things we are learning. We can set up an "Anger Buster Center" in our house with some of these materials so I'll have a place to go when I'm angry.

If you would like to speak with the counselor, please call (________)________________.

____
YOUR CHILD

ANGER-MANAGEMENT GROUP STUDENT EVALUATION

NAME ______________________________ DATE __________

TEACHER ______________________________

Please answer the following questions about the Anger-Management Group **HONESTLY**:

1. I enjoyed coming to the counselor's office. (Please circle one.)

   A LOT **A LITTLE** **NOT AT ALL**

2. I learned things in this group that I didn't already know. (Please circle one.)

   A LOT **A LITTLE** **NOT AT ALL**

3. The thing I liked best about this group was:

   ____

   ____

4. The thing I didn't like about this group was:

   ____

   ____

5. Three (3) things I learned in this group were:

   A. ______________________________

   ____

   B. ______________________________

   ____

   C. ______________________________

   ____

6. I would like to be a member of another group with the counselor. (Please circle one.)

   A LOT **A LITTLE** **NOT AT ALL**

DIVORCE

SMALL-GROUP COUNSELING

Statistics prove that many children are children of divorce. Educators see these children on a daily basis and their behaviors often indicate a need for additional support from a professional staff member.

THIS SECTION INCLUDES:

Reproducible Parent Handouts
Suggested Activities
Reproducible Poster
Reproducible Student Evaluation Sheet

Divorce Group Parent Permission Form (page 157) **SG PH**

Distribute this sheet to parents of all children in the targeted grade levels.

Suggested Divorce Activities Grades 1-5 (pages 158-159) **SG SA**

These three suggested activities for use in small groups include a follow-up *In The Counselor's Office, I Learned* student handout (page 159) summarizing the issues discussed.

Post Divorce Small-Group Counseling Letters For Parents (pages 160-161) **SG PH**

Sending letters to parents at the end of small-group counseling sessions is courteous and appreciated.

Divorce Group Student Evaluation (page 162) **SG SH**

Feedback from students is an invaluable resource that helps counselors plan for future group sessions. Distribute the evaluation sheet at the final group meeting.

Dear Parents:

I will be initiating DIVORCE small-group counseling sessions in the next month. During these sessions, we will discuss how children whose parents divorce are not alone, how whatever they feel is okay, how to make the most of living in two houses, how divorce is not their fault, and how much their parents love them.

These sessions will meet once a week for ________ weeks. The ___-minute group may not be held on consecutive weeks, due to field trips, assemblies, holidays, etc.

If you feel issues regarding the divorce are interfering with your child's academics, please sign the following permission form and return it to your child's teacher by ___________________________. The first group session will begin as soon as an appropriate schedule is worked out with your child's classroom teacher.

I would like to help you and your child make the rest of the school year as successful as possible. If you would like to discuss your child, or you have any questions or concerns, please do not hesitate to contact me.

Sincerely,

____

WE CARE ABOUT KIDS

I, ___________________________________, give permission for my child to participate in the DIVORCE GROUP with the counselor.

Child's Name ________________________________ Date __________

School ____________________________________ Grade _________

Teacher ___________________________________

Home Phone (_______) ________________________

Work Phone (_______) ________________________

Parent's Printed Name _________________________

Parent's Signature ____________________________

SUGGESTED DIVORCE ACTIVITIES
GRADES 1-5

DIVORCE ACTIVITY #1:

On the chalkboard or a piece of chart paper, draw a picture of a house. Tell the children it is a picture of the house where their mothers lived when they were little girls. Draw two parents and a little girl in the house. Tell the children that their grandparents had certain rules for their mothers to follow when they were growing up, such as not eating dinner in front of the television. Write a few rules above the picture of the house.

Draw a picture of another house. Tell the children it is a picture of the house where their fathers lived when they were little boys. Draw two parents and a little boy in the house. Tell the children that their grandparents had certain rules for their fathers to follow when they were growing up, such as it was okay to eat dinner while watching television. (Make the rules different than those listed above the mother's house.) Write a few rules above the picture of the house.

Draw a picture of a house with a mother and a father inside. Tell the children:

> *Your parents grew up, fell in love, and got married. Before you were born, your parents sometimes argued because their rules didn't match. Mom might say, "I don't think we should watch TV while we are eating dinner."* Then Dad might say, *"Why not? My family always watched TV while eating dinner."* (Draw a picture of the child in the house. Explain to the children that their parents grew up with different rules. Those rules were neither good nor bad, they were just different. Parents may argue when they disagree about rules.) *They loved you very much, but they continued to argue. Did you cause them to argue? No! They argued even before you were born. They continued to argue so much that they decided they would be happier if they did not live in the same house any more. They got a divorce from each other, but they did not get a divorce from you!"*

DIVORCE ACTIVITY #2:

Have each child draw a picture of their mom's house and their dad's house. Ask the children to list two fun things they do at each house and two things they wish they could change at each house. Have volunteers show and discuss their pictures.

DIVORCE ACTIVITY #3:

Discuss how the children feel when their parents argue. Talk about where, when, and why parents argue and what the children can do so they do not have to listen to the arguing. Discuss going to their room, listening to music, playing outside, etc. Have the children draw four places they can go to get away from arguing. Have volunteers discuss their pictures. In addition, if one parent has a habit of talking negatively about the other parent, have the children practice saying, "Please do not talk about Mom/Dad that way."

In the Counselors Office, I Learned

1. Divorce is NOT my fault.

2. If Mom or Dad says something bad about the other one, I should say, "Please do not talk about Mom/Dad that way."

3. It's okay to feel sad, happy, or mad about divorce. I can feel anything I want to feel.

4. If Mom and Dad start arguing, I should go somewhere where I cannot hear them and play a game, listen to music, or watch TV.

Dear ____,

I have been to the counselor's office to talk about divorce. I learned that:

1. I do fun things with both Mom and Dad and it is okay to tell one parent I had fun at the other parent's house. Both of you want me to be happy wherever I am.

2. Both Mom and Dad love me and want me to be happy.

3. Divorce is definitely NOT my fault! It is an adult decision my parents have made.

4. Children want their parents to live together. They hope, if they are "good," their parents will get back together again, but this is not true.

5. Any feeling I have is okay. I drew a picture of my houses and my families and talked about how I felt about divorce.

6. If I hear my parents arguing, I can go to my room and listen to music or play a game.

7. Lots of children have divorced parents.
I am not the only one.

Please talk with me about these things at home.

Love,

____

Dear ______________________________,

I have been visiting the counselor's office to discuss divorce. I have learned the following things:

1. There are good things and bad things about divorce.
2. Divorce is NOT my fault.
3. Lots of other kids are going through a divorce, too.
4. If you argue, I can go to my room, go outside, or listen to music.
5. If one of you talks badly about the other, I will say, "Please don't talk about Mom/Dad that way."
6. You DID NOT divorce me, you divorced each other.

Please talk with me about the things we learned and help me practice expressing my feelings.

If you would like to speak with the counselor, please call ____________________.

Love,

____
YOUR CHILD

DIVORCE GROUP STUDENT EVALUATION

NAME ______________________ DATE __________

TEACHER ______________________

Please answer the following questions about the Divorce Group **HONESTLY**:

1. I enjoyed coming to the counselor's office. (Please circle one.)

   A LOT **A LITTLE** **NOT AT ALL**

2. I learned things in this group that I didn't already know. (Please circle one.)

   A LOT **A LITTLE** **NOT AT ALL**

3. The thing I liked best about this group was:

   ____

   ____

4. The thing I didn't like about this group was:

   ____

   ____

5. Three (3) things I learned in this group were:

   A. ______________________

   ____

   B. ______________________

   ____

   C. ______________________

   ____

6. I would like to be a member of another group with the counselor. (Please circle one.)

   A LOT **A LITTLE** **NOT AT ALL**

GRIEF & LOSS

SMALL-GROUP COUNSELING

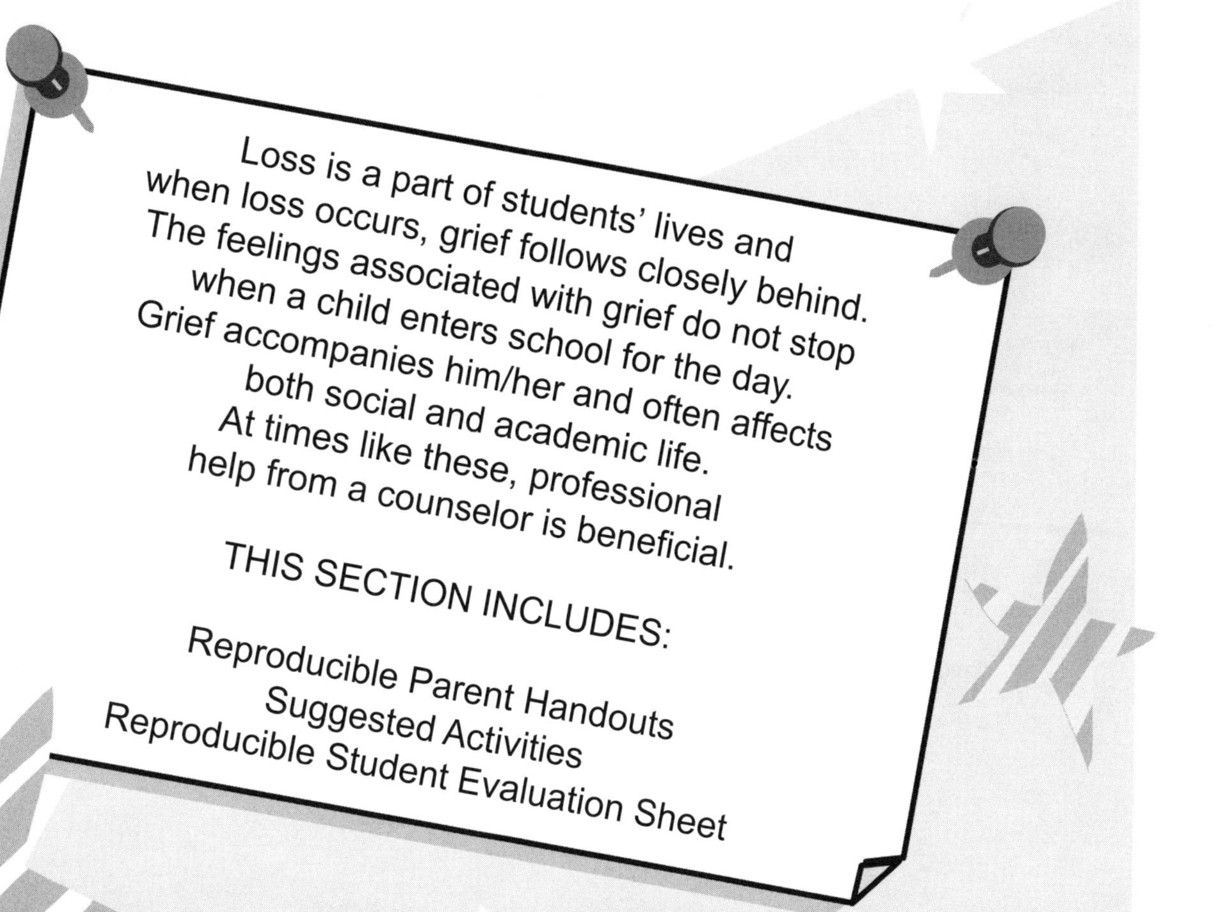

Grief And Loss Group Parent Permission Form (page 165) **SG** **PH**

Distribute this sheet to parents of all children in the targeted grade levels.

Suggested Grief And Loss Activities Grades 1-5 (page 166) **SG** **SA**

Three suggested activities for use in small groups.

Post Grief And Loss Small-Group Counseling Letter For Parents (page 167) **SG** **PH**

Sending letters to parents at the end of small-group counseling sessions is courteous and appreciated.

Grief And Loss Group Student Evaluation (page 168) **SG** **SH**

Feedback from students is an invaluable resource that helps counselors plan for future group sessions. Distribute the evaluation sheet at the final group meeting.

Dear Parents,

I will be initiating GRIEF AND LOSS small-group counseling sessions in the next month. This group is for students who have experienced a death. We will discuss our losses and the stages of grief. We will make memory boxes about our loved ones to share with the other members of the group, and we will learn that all of our feelings are okay.

These sessions will meet once a week for ________ weeks. The ___-minute group may not be held on consecutive weeks, due to field trips, assemblies, holidays, etc.

If you feel issues regarding your child's loss are interfering with his/her academics, please sign the following permission form and return it to your child's teacher by ____________________________. The first group session will begin as soon as an appropriate schedule is worked out with your child's classroom teacher.

I would like to help you and your child make the rest of the school year as successful as possible. If you would like to discuss your child, or you have any questions or concerns, please do not hesitate to contact me.

Sincerely,

____

WE CARE ABOUT KIDS

I, ____________________________________, give permission for my child to participate in the GRIEF AND LOSS GROUP with the counselor.

Child's Name ____________________________________ Date ___________

School ____________________________________ Grade __________

Teacher ____________________________________

Home Phone (_______) ________________________

Work Phone (_______) ________________________

Parent's Printed Name ________________________

Parent's Signature ____________________________

SUGGESTED GRIEF AND LOSS ACTIVITIES
GRADES 1-5

These activities can be used as guidelines for facilitating a small-group counseling session.

GRIEF AND LOSS ACTIVITY #I:

Have the students tell what special things they did with the person who died. Have them draw and paint pictures of themselves and their loved ones doing these special things. Mount their pictures with glue onto colored construction paper to make the picture look very special. Have each student share his/her picture with the group. Tell the students to place the picture in a place where they can see it when they feel sad.

GRIEF AND LOSS ACTIVITY #2:

Before the group begins, cut out three circles for each group member. Read a story about feelings or have the students name different feelings they have had. If the students are naming feelings, have them continue to contribute until the list is age-appropriate. Discuss different feelings with the students and stress that all feelings are okay. Tell the students that they may have many different feelings when someone dies. They may feel mad that the person died, sad because they will miss the person, happy that the person no longer feels sick, etc. Give each student three circles and crayons or markers. Tell the students to think about how they felt when their loved one died. Ask the students to draw a feeling face on each circle that represents how they felt when their loved one died. When everyone has finished, have the students share their drawings with the group. As they share each drawing, use masking tape to attach each circle to their clothing. When all of the feeling faces have been shared, remind the students that every feeling they have is okay.

GRIEF AND LOSS ACTIVITY 3:

Discuss how people have been treating the children since the death of their loved one. Ask them if their friends, teachers, and relatives have been treating them differently. Explain that some people feel very sad for them and are not sure what to say to help them feel better. Have the students describe how they feel about being treated differently. Hang a piece of chart paper on the wall, then have the students formulate a list of what they wish people would say to them or what they wish people would do to help them feel a little better. Include things that people have done that the students appreciated. Allow them to copy the list and share it with their friends and family members.

Dear ______________________________,

I have been visiting the counselor's office to discuss death. I have learned the following things:

1. All of my feelings are okay.
2. It is okay to talk about the death even though it may make others sad.
3. There are many wonderful things about the person who died.
4. I can look at my memory box any time I feel sad.
5. I will slowly begin to feel better and I will laugh a little more each day.
6. Some people may feel less sad very quickly. Other people may feel sad for a long time.

Please talk with me about the things I have learned and help me practice expressing my feelings.

If you would like to speak with the counselor, please call ______________________.

Love,

____
YOUR CHILD

GRIEF AND LOSS GROUP STUDENT EVALUATION

NAME ______________________________ DATE ____________

TEACHER ______________________________

Please answer the following questions about the Grief and Loss Group **HONESTLY**:

1. I enjoyed coming to the counselor's office. (Please circle one.)

   A LOT **A LITTLE** **NOT AT ALL**

2. I learned things in this group that I didn't already know. (Please circle one.)

   A LOT **A LITTLE** **NOT AT ALL**

3. The thing I liked best about this group was:

   ____

   ____

4. The thing I didn't like about this group was:

   ____

   ____

5. Three (3) things I learned in this group were:

   A. ______________________________

   ____

   B. ______________________________

   ____

   C. ______________________________

   ____

6. I would like to be a member of another group with the counselor. (Please circle one.)

   A LOT **A LITTLE** **NOT AT ALL**

CAREER AWARENESS

CLASSROOM GUIDANCE
SCHOOL-WIDE PROGRAM

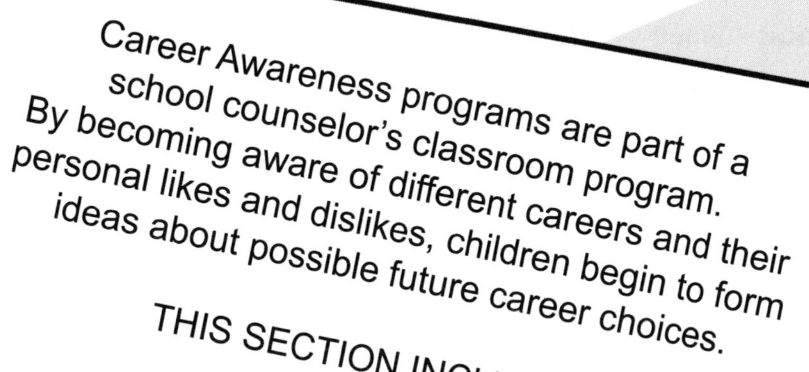

Career Awareness Lesson Plan I Grades 2-5 (pages 172-173) **CG**

This sample lesson plan may be presented to classrooms.

Your Present ... Your Future (page 174) **CG SH**

This activity may be adapted to any grade level. Kindergarten and first-grade students can perform it orally as a group. Second- through fifth-graders can do the exercise independently.

Career Awareness Lesson Plan II Grades 2-5 (pages 175-176) **CG**

This sample lesson plan may be presented to classrooms.

Career Trash Can Basketball Questions (page 177) **CG**

Reproduce these questions for the leader to use when playing *Career Trash Can Basketball.*

Career Awareness Lesson Plan Grades 3-5 (page 178) **CG**

This sample lesson plan may be presented to classrooms.

Career Sundae (pages 179-180) **CG SH**

Students select the career of their choice and name the tools, characteristics, and education needed for the job as well as the duties of the job. When they have finished, they illustrate their findings in the form of an ice cream sundae.

What Do You Want To Be
When You Grow Up? Poster (page 181) **CG SH**

Reproduce the poster for each student.

Career Awareness Student Evaluation (page 182) **CG SH**

Reproduce the evaluation sheet for each student. Have the students complete it at the end of the Career Guidance unit.

Career Day (page 183) **CG SW SH**

This Career Day format may be used for second through fifth grades. Reproduce the activity sheet for each student and tell the students to select the career of their choice and do research to obtain the information needed to answer the questions on the activity sheet. Set a date for the Career Day. On that day, each student is to dress as if he/she actually had the job of his/her choice and share what he/she learned with a younger grade level.

Teacher Inventory Letter (page 184) **SW TH**

Teacher involvement promotes cooperation and that is essential for a successful school store. Distribute this letter to each teacher, giving him/her the opportunity to note the supplies students run out of most often and the supplies they prefer not to have available. This letter can help determine which supplies teachers prefer before placing the initial supply order.

Student Job Application (page 185) **CG SH**

Before beginning to work at the school store, students should complete an application just as they would do if applying for a job outside of school. Distribute this form to all potential "employees." The counselor should interview all applicants.

Grand-Opening Flier (page 186) **SW PH**

This flier can be sent home to all parents informing them of the new school store, the supplies offered, and the prices. Complete the questions and list the supplies and their prices before reproducing the flier for parents. The list suggested on the flier may need to be changed to fit your needs. No prices were included, as prices will vary from locale to locale and must be appropriate for the one in which the school store will be located.

Supply List (page 187) **SW**

Make a list of all supplies and their prices and post this advertisement in various places throughout the school. The list suggested on this flier may need to be changed to fit your needs. No prices were included, as prices will vary from locale to locale and must be appropriate for the one in which the school store will be located.

CAREER AWARENESS LESSON PLAN I
GRADES 2-5

Materials Needed:

- ☐ Copy of *Your Present … Your Future* (page 174) for each student
- ☐ Pencil and crayons for each student
- ☐ Chalkboard and chalk or dry erase board and marker

Pre-Presentation Preparation:

Reproduce a copy of *Your Present … Your Future* for each student.

Presentation:

- Introduce the lesson by asking:

  How many different kinds of jobs do you think there are in the world? (Pause for students' answers.)

- Go to the board and write the numeral 4. Then ask the students if they think there are more than four jobs in the world. Write a 0 behind the 4. Then ask the students if they think there are more than 40 jobs in the world. Do the same for 400, 4,000, and 40,000. At this point, tell the students that there are more than 40,000 different jobs in the world.

- Ask the students:

  Have you ever read the label on the back of a shampoo bottle? (Pause for answers.)

  The words on the back of a shampoo bottle were written by a copywriter who must make sure the shampoo is described correctly and the directions are clear and easy to understand.

  You may choose to be anything you want to be when you grow up. It is very likely that you will change your minds many times between now and then.

  When choosing a job, there are only two rules that you should follow. You should like the job you choose and you should choose something you do well.

It is very possible that you will have more than one career when you are an adult. For example, some school counselors are teachers first, then become counselors. Some then become principals and even superintendents.

- Distribute *Your Present ... Your Future,* a pencil, and crayons to each student. Review the questions before having the students begin. Then have them complete the questions and draw and color the two pictures at the bottom of the page.
- When everyone has finished, have the students share their work with the class.
- You may want to ask the classroom teacher if you can display the papers in the classroom or you may send the papers home with the students.

YOUR PRESENT ... YOUR FUTURE

Name ______________________ Date ______________

1. What is your favorite thing to do? ______________________

2. Why do you like doing that so much? ______________________

____

3. What do you do really well in school? ______________________

4. What do you do really well at home? ______________________

5. What would you like to be doing when you are 20 years old? Why? ______________________

____

____

6. What would you like to be doing when you are 40 years old? Why? ______________________

____

____

7. What are you learning now that will help you with that job? ______________________

____

DRAW A PICTURE OF YOURSELF AT 20 YEARS OF AGE.

DRAW A PICTURE OF YOURSELF AT 40 YEARS OF AGE.

CAREER AWARENESS LESSON PLAN II

GRADES 2-5

Materials Needed:

- ☐ Copy of *Career Trash Can Basketball Questions* (page 177) for the leader
- ☐ Trash can
- ☐ Any ball (kickball, basketball, tennis ball, etc.)
- ☐ Chalkboard and chalk or dry-erase board and marker
- ☐ Piece of tape

Pre-Presentation Preparation:

Place a trash can in the front of the classroom.

Draw a team scoreboard on the board.

Decide where the student who is shooting the basket should stand. Place a piece of tape on the spot on the floor where the student is to stand.

Presentation:

- Divide the students into two teams.
- Ask for a volunteer from one team to be the catcher and stand behind the trash can. Explain that the ball cannot be caught *above* the trash can, but only behind it or on its sides.
- Ask for a volunteer from the other team to keep score at the board.
- Tell the students:

  Each team will send one student to the front of the room at a time. I will ask that person a question. If the student answers the question correctly, he or she will get a point and get the chance to earn a bonus point by making the basket. (Note: Try to give lots of clues to any student who does not know the answer. The purpose of this lesson is to teach and review the concepts. It is not intended to be a major competition between the two teams.)

- Have one student from the first team come to the front of the room. Ask the student a question. If the question is answered correctly, the scorekeeper gives the team a point. Then the student stands at the tape on the floor and attempts to throw the ball and make a basket. If the student makes a basket, the scorekeeper gives the team another point.

- Continue the game until everyone has had a turn. Remember at the end to give both the catcher and the scorekeeper a turn.

- The team that earns the most points is the winner.

CAREER TRASH CAN BASKETBALL QUESTIONS

1. For what career would you have to know a lot about animals?
2. For what career do you have to be a good decorator?
3. What career makes flowers look even prettier?
4. For what career do you have to know a lot about books?
5. For what career do you have to use a ruler?
6. For what career do you work with jewelry?
7. What career do you work with make-up?
8. For what career do you need to know a lot about computers?
9. For what career do you need to be good with children?
10. For what career do you need to be good at speaking in front of others?
11. For what career do you need to work with pipes and water?
12. What do you have to do well to be a librarian?
13. What do you have to do well to be a veterinarian?
14. What do you have to do well to be a doctor?
15. What do you have to do well to be a coach?
16. What do you have to do well to be a scientist?
17. What do you have to do well to be a police officer?
18. What do you have to do well to be a firefighter?
19. What do you have to do well to be a nurse?
20. What tools would you use if you were a chef?
21. What tools would you use if you were a hairstylist?
22. What tools would you use if you were a clothes designer?
23. What tools would you use if you were an artist?
24. What tools would you use if you were a dentist?
25. What tools would you use if you were a salesperson?
26. For what career do you have to be a good map reader?
27. For what career do you have to not be afraid of heights?
28. For what career do you have to have a good memory?
29. What do you have to do well to be a carpenter?
30. What do you have to do well to be a pharmacist?
31. What do you have to do well to be a professional athlete?
32. What tools would you use if you were a musician?
33. What tools would you use if you were a letter carrier?
34. What tools would you use if you were an automobile mechanic?

CAREER AWARENESS LESSON PLAN
GRADES 3-5

Materials Needed:

- ☐ Copy of *Career Sundae* (pages 179-180) for each student
- ☐ Copy of *What Do You Want To Be When You Grow Up?* poster (page 181) for each student
- ☐ Construction paper, glue, scissors, pencil, and crayons or markers for each student

Pre-Presentation Preparation:

Reproduce a copy of *Career Sundae* and *What Do You Want To Be When You Grow Up?* for each student.

Presentation:

- Tell the students:

  [illegible] ant to be when you grow up. It should be something you [illegible] g you do well.

  [illegible] on, there will be many things to think about. Think about [illegible] ne education you will need, and the everyday responsi-[illegible]

- Di[illegible] construction paper, glue, scissors, a pencil, and crayons or ma[illegible] n say:

  You will each be making a Career Sundae. *Each part of the sundae will represent a different part of the job you are thinking you might like. As you read the directions, you will fill out parts of the sundae with different parts of the job you selected. Then you will cut out the parts and glue them to the construction paper.*

- When everyone has finished, have volunteers share their sundaes with the class, then display them in the classroom.

- Distribute a *What Do You Want To Be When You Grow Up?* poster to each child to take home.

CAREER SUNDAE

1. Think of a job you might like to have when you are older.
2. Write the **name of the job** on the **ice cream dish.**
3. Write the **education** you will need for the job on the **whipped cream**.
4. Write **3 duties or responsibilities** a person has while doing this job on the **ice cream.**
5. Write 3 things you would **need to do well** to do this job on the **hot fudge**.
6. Write **3 tools** you would use to do this job on the **strawberries**.
7. **Color** the sundae and cut out the pieces of the sundae and the sundae dish.
8. **Glue** the pieces to the construction paper.
9. ***CONGRATULATIONS!***
   You have made a Career Sundae!

CAREER SUNDAE

What Do You Want To Be When You Grow Up?

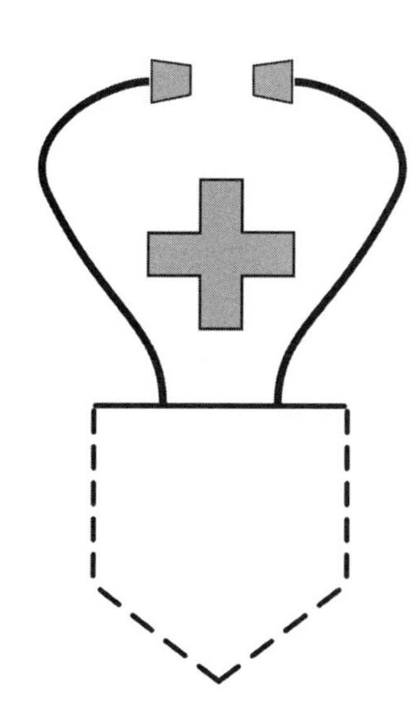

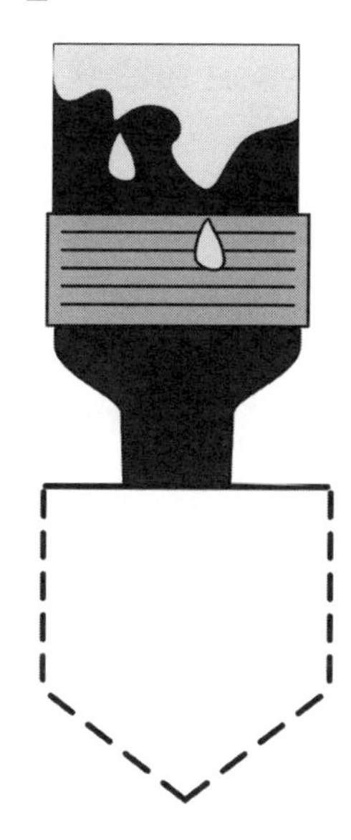

Just Remember To...

Like it!

and

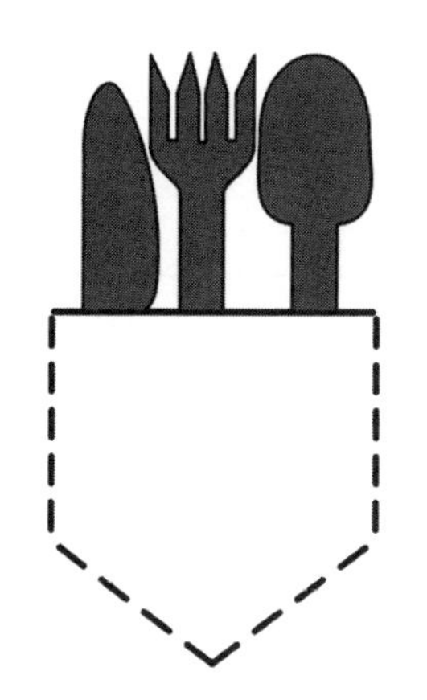

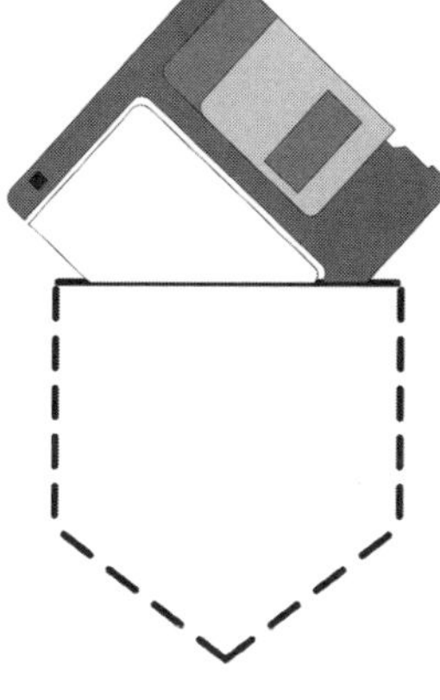

Be good at it!

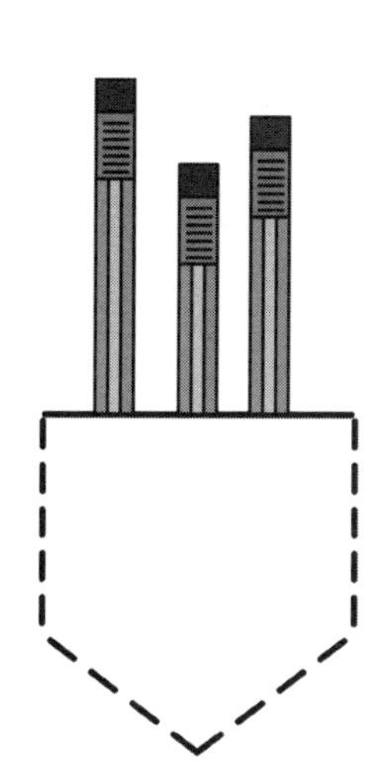

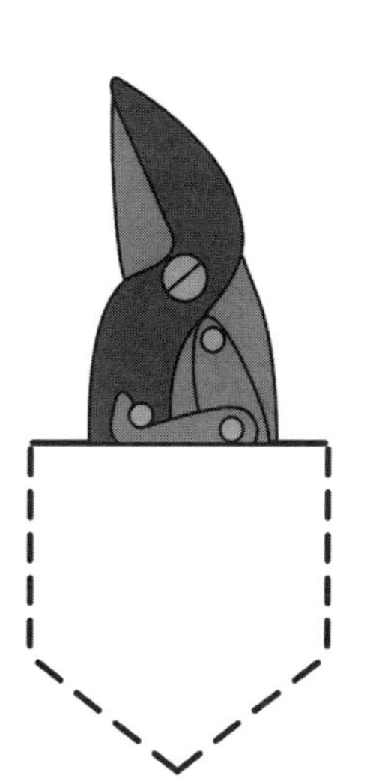

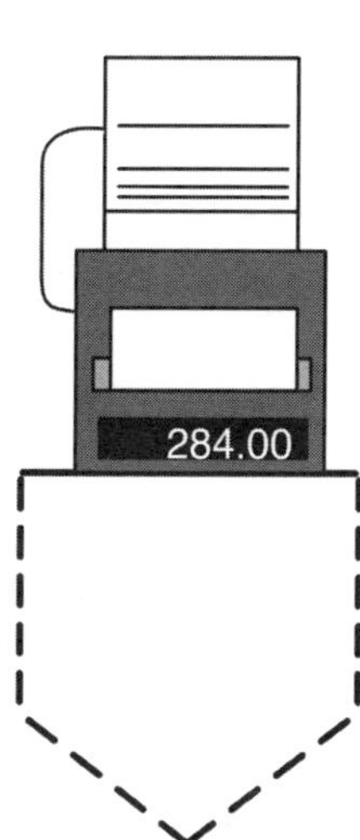

CAREER AWARENESS STUDENT EVALUATION

NAME ______________________________ DATE ____________

TEACHER ______________________________

Please answer the following questions about the Career Awareness unit **HONESTLY**:

1. I enjoyed the counselor coming to the classroom. (Please circle one.)

   A LOT   **A LITTLE**   **NOT AT ALL**

2. I learned things in this class that I didn't already know. (Please circle one.)

   A LOT   **A LITTLE**   **NOT AT ALL**

3. The thing I liked best about this class was:

   ____

   ____

4. The thing I didn't like about this class was:

   ____

   ____

5. Three (3) things I learned in this class were:

   A. ______________________________

   ____

   B. ______________________________

   ____

   C. ______________________________

   ____

Date__________

Name____

1. When I grow up, I may want to be a____________

   ____.

2. I think I would be good at this job because _____

   ____

   ____.

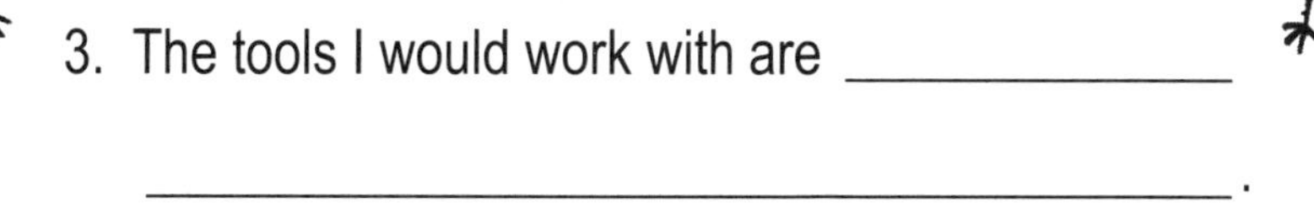

3. The tools I would work with are ______________

   ____.

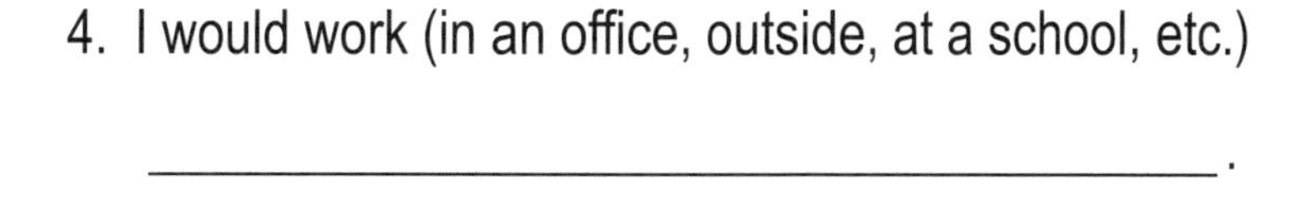

4. I would work (in an office, outside, at a school, etc.)

   ____.

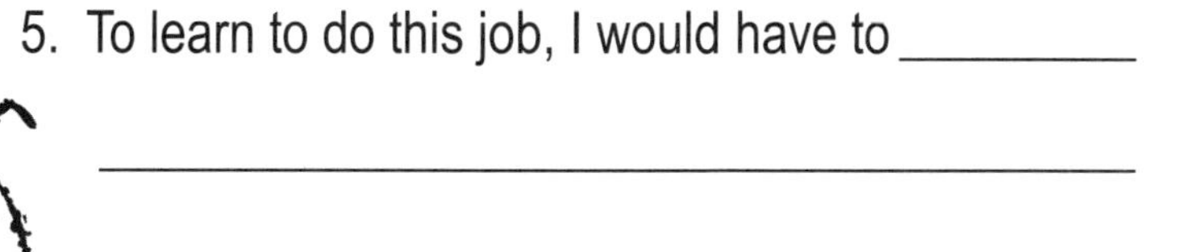

5. To learn to do this job, I would have to_________

   ____

   ____

   ____.

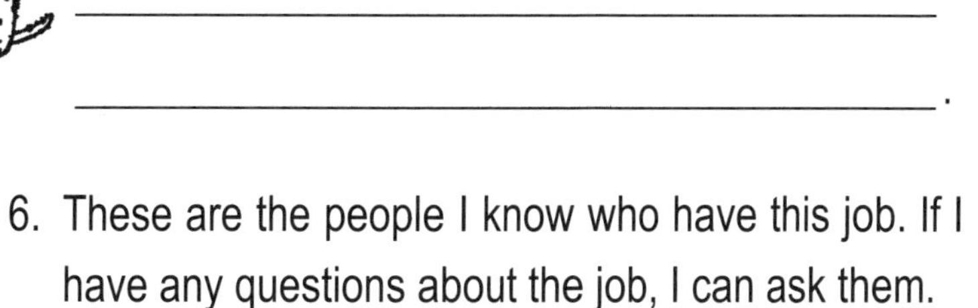

6. These are the people I know who have this job. If I have any questions about the job, I can ask them.

   ____

   ____

Big News

Dear Teachers:

We are opening a school store on ____________. Every__________________, school supplies will be sold from the store from _______ to _______ o'clock. At first, I will set up and run the store by myself. After the store "gets off the ground," I will be asking certain students to help me order and sell merchandise and count money. Those students helping me will learn about supply and demand, economics, and career concepts. Being part of this project will be a positive reward for students with good behavior.

I am sure there are specific supplies you DO NOT want your students to have and supplies that frequently run out. Please list these below so I will not go against your class rules when ordering. In addition, please write whether you would like the students to check into their classroom before coming to the store or you would like them to get their supplies first.

Thank you for your time and cooperation.

Teacher's name ____

SUPPLIES WE WANT THE STORE TO SELL	SUPPLIES WE DON'T WANT THE STORE TO SELL
____________________	____________________
____________________	____________________
____________________	____________________
____________________	____________________
____________________	____________________
____________________	____________________

Please check one:

☐ Students should go to the store before they come to class.

☐ Students should go to the store after they check in at the classroom.

Additional Suggestions:

____

____

____

SCHOOL STORE

NAME

SCHOOL

TEACHER

GRADE

STUDENT JOB APPLICATION

What time do you arrive at school in the morning?

____

If hired, how would you treat our customers? ____________________________________

____

____

Why do you think you would be a good employee? ____________________________________

____

____

Why do you want to work at our school store? ____________________________________

____

____

I promise I have been very honest when answering these questions, and I promise to do my very best as an employee in our school store.

Student's Signature ______________________________ Date ____________

Parent's Signature ______________________________

Please understand this job will not be for the rest of the school year. Every few weeks, someone else will be chosen so that many students will have a chance to work in the store. If you are hired, I will tell you which mornings you will be employed. You will receive a pencil or eraser of your choice for every morning you work. Thank you.

What? ______________________________

Where? ______________________________

Why? To sell supplies in the event a student runs out of something

What To Do? If your child needs supplies, please send a list and money in a plastic bag so the money will not be confused with lunch money. If the list is long, I will help your child shop.

ITEMS AVAILABLE AND COST:

- ✔ Crayons (Box of 16) $ ______
- ✔ Colored Pencils $ ______
- ✔ Erasers (Small) $ ______
- ✔ Erasers (Large) $ ______
- ✔ Folders $ ______
- ✔ Glue Sticks $ ______
- ✔ Highlighters $ ______
- ✔ Markers $ ______
- ✔ Pens $ ______
- ✔ Notebooks (Steno) $ ______
- ✔ Notebook Paper (100 Sheets) $ ______
- ✔ Rulers $ ______

Please stop by and see us!

SUPPLY LIST

- ✔ Notebook Paper (100 Sheets) $ _____
- ✔ Notebooks (Steno) $ _____
- ✔ Crayons (Box of 16) $ _____
- ✔ Colored Pencils $ _____
- ✔ Erasers (Small) $ _____
- ✔ Erasers (Large) $ _____
- ✔ Folders $ _____
- ✔ Glue Sticks $ _____
- ✔ Highlighters $ _____
- ✔ Markers $ _____
- ✔ Pens $ _____
- ✔ Rulers $ _____

VISIT THE SCHOOL STORE!

DRUG AWARENESS

CLASSROOM GUIDANCE
SCHOOL-WIDE PROGRAM

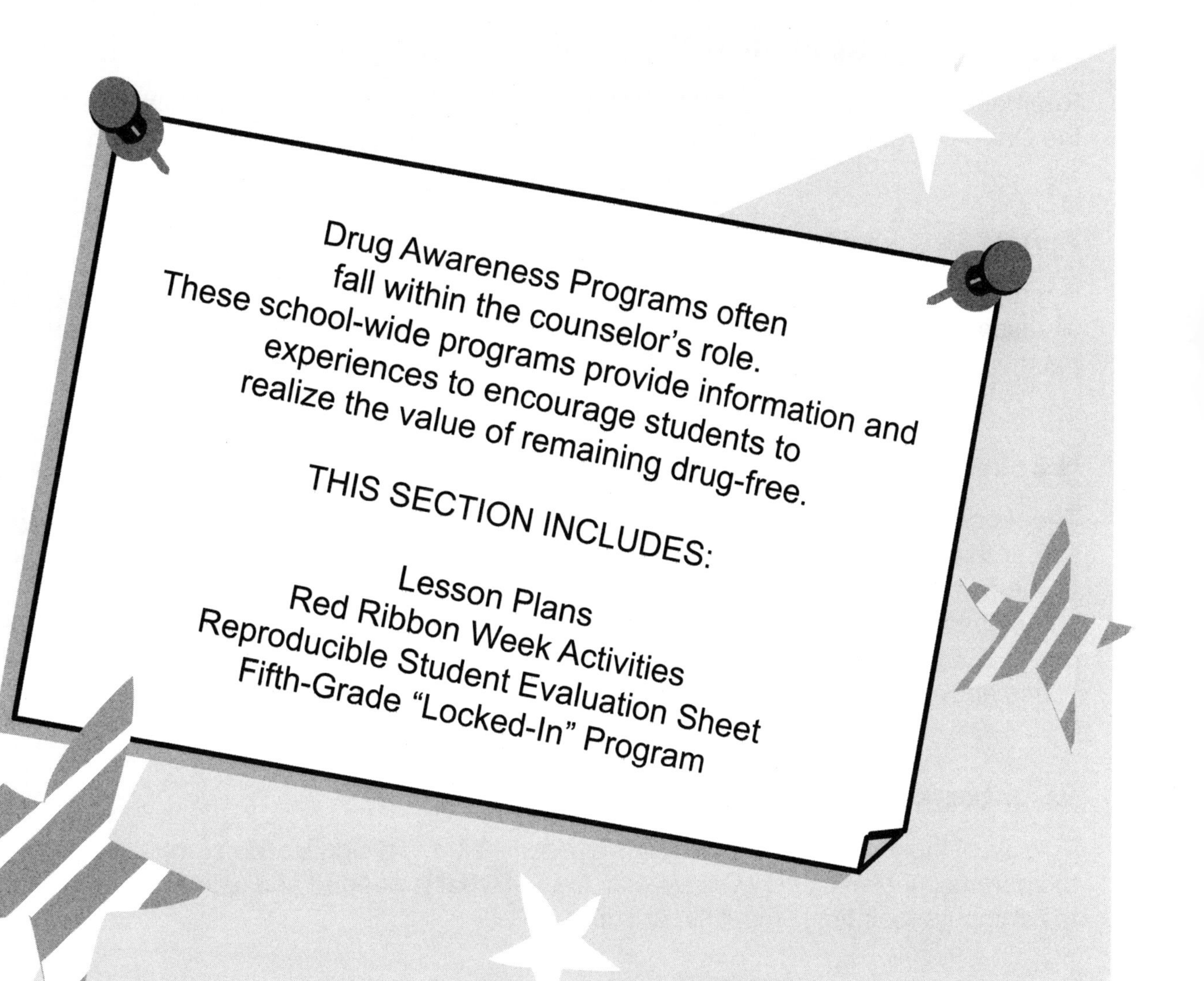

Drug Awareness Lesson Plan Grades PK-1 (pages 192-193) **CG**

This sample lesson plan may be presented to classrooms.

Drug Awareness Lesson Plan I Grades 2-5 (pages 194-196) **CG**

This sample lesson plan may be presented to classrooms.

Drug Awareness Lesson Plan II Grades 2-5 (pages 197-198) **CG**

This sample lesson plan may be presented to classrooms.

Drug-Free Trash Can Basketball Questions (page 199) **CG**

Reproduce these questions for the leader to use when playing *Drug-Free Trash Can Basketball.*

Drug Awareness Student Evaluation (page 200) **CG SH**

Reproduce the evaluation sheet for each student. Have the students complete it at the end of the Drug Awareness guidance unit.

Parent Letters Regarding Red Ribbon Activities (pages 201-202) **PH**

Reproduce these letters or use them as guidelines and personalize them for your particular situation. The letters sent home to parents at the end of September should explain all the planned activities leading up to National Red Ribbon Week.

"Locked-In" On Refusing Drugs Activity (pages 203-204) **PH**

The "Lock-In" is a special night for a specific grade level. Students in this grade are invited to school to participate in activities that promote drug awareness. The night can end at midnight or the following morning, after a sleepover. This flier explains the program's objectives and should be placed in a packet containing all the information sent home to each student's parents. Prior to reproducing the flier on page 204, write the appropriate grade level in the white space above the key.

Volunteers And Supplies Needed (pages 205-206) **PH**

This list of the volunteers and supplies needed includes a sign-up form for parents. Place it in the parents' packet so they will have an idea of what is needed and whether they will be able to contribute their time, supplies, or both.

"Locked-In" On Refusing Drugs Schedule (pages 207-208) **CG PH**

These two forms are examples of possible schedules. One includes the time schedule. The other does not. The evening "Lock-In" times were left blank so the user could personalize the schedule. The sleepover schedule includes the times because this format was not discussed in the previous forms. The selected schedule should be reviewed with the students and a copy should be placed in the packet sent home to parents.

Acts Of Community Service
Required To Attend "Lock-In" (page 209) **CG PH**

This form provides information about possible community service projects and details on how the project is to be summarized. Although created for the "Lock-In" project, this form may be used for other community service projects. Reproduce the form for the students and put a form in the packet sent home to parents.

Student "Lock-In" Permission Form (page 210) **PH**

Fill in the date that the form must be returned to the counselor. Then reproduce copies and place one in each packet sent home to parents.

Thank You Letters For Volunteers And Donations (pages 211-212) **PH**

These letters may be reproduced for those who volunteered and organizations that donated items for the raffle.

DRUG AWARENESS LESSON PLAN
GRADES PK-1

Materials Needed:

- ☐ Doctor's costume or dress-up outfit
- ☐ Nurse's costume or dress-up outfit
- ☐ Sunglasses for the "teenager" outfit
- ☐ Briefcase and tie for the "dad" outfit
- ☐ Briefcase and purse for the "mom" outfit
- ☐ Friend outfit
- ☐ Six brown grocery-type bags
- ☐ Stickers for each student

Pre-Presentation Preparation:

Place each outfit or costume in a separate bag. Label each bag with the name of the costume such as doctor, nurse, teenager, friend, Dad, Mom.

Presentation:

- Introduce the lesson by asking:

  What do you do when you are sick? (Go to the doctor, stay in bed, take medicine, and any other appropriate answers.)

  Who can tell us about a time you were sick and had to take medicine?

  Who gave you the medicine?

  Why should you never take medicine by yourself? (Medicine is taken differently by people of different weights and different ages. Moms and Dads know how to read the directions and give their children medicine safely.)

- Ask for six volunteers, making sure you have at least one boy to be the dad and one girl to be the mother. The other characters are not gender-specific.

- Take the six volunteers into the hall and give each student a bag. Tell the students to quietly put on the costume that is in their bag. When the students have put on the costumes, have them knock on the classroom door.

- Return to the classroom and tell the students they are going to have some "visitors." Have several children try to guess who the visitors will be.

- When the volunteers have put on their costumes, have them line up facing the class audience.

- The volunteers should put their bags in front of them. The labels telling the name of the person each volunteer is pretending to be should face the audience.

- Tell the students that the visitors are a doctor, a nurse, a friend, a teenager, a mom, and a dad.

- Ask the "doctor" to step to the front of the line. Then ask the class:

  Can a doctor safely give you medicine? (Yes.)

  Why is it safe for a doctor to give you medicine? (Doctors know what makes you sick and what makes you well. Doctors know how to read directions and can tell you what amount of medicine you should take.)

- Ask the "friend" to step to the front of the line. Then ask the class:

  Can a friend safely give you medicine? (No.)

  Why isn't it safe for a friend to give you medicine? (Friends may not know how to read directions correctly and could give you the wrong amount of medicine. That could make you even sicker. You should never take a chance when taking medicine.)

- Continue this process with the "nurse," "teenager," "mom," and "dad."

- When all the presentations have been made, have the "audience" applaud the actors.

- Tell the children:

  I am going to walk around and ask each of you a question. If you answer the question correctly, I will give you a sticker.

- Ask each child to name two people who can give him/her medicine safely. As each child answers correctly, give him/her a sticker.

DRUG AWARENESS LESSON PLAN I
GRADES 2-5

Materials Needed:

- ☐ Poster of body outline or chart paper
- ☐ Copy of *Drug Awareness* for each student (page 196)
- ☐ Pencil and crayons for each student
- ☐ Tape
- ☐ Black and red marker

Pre-Presentation Preparation:

If you are using chart paper, draw an outline of a body with the black marker. Hang the poster or chart paper in the front of the room where all of the students can see it. Reproduce a copy of *Drug Awareness* for each student.

Presentation:

- Introduce the lesson by asking:

  Have you ever smelled cigarette smoke? How did you think it smelled? Why? (Accept any appropriate answer.)

  Why is smoking cigarettes dangerous? (There are hundreds of very harmful ingredients in cigarettes (paint thinner [acetone], floor cleaner [ammonia], rat poison [arsenic], carbon monoxide, sewer gas [methane], rocket fuel [methanol], etc.) These harmful chemicals and poisons really hurt the body.)

- Using a black marker, draw smoke going into the mouth and chest on the body you have drawn.

- Beginning with the fingers, ask the students how cigarettes affect the different parts of the body. Use the information provided below, making appropriate selections for the grade level to which the information is being presented. Circle each part in red as it is discussed:

  Fingers: Skin yellows and hands smell

  Eyes: Become dry, bloodshot, watery (Heavy smokers are at risk for developing cataracts. Smokers also have twice the risk of nonsmokers for developing macular degeneration, an age-related eye disorder.)

Nose: Becomes dry inside and loses sense of smell

Lips: Become chapped, cracked, and wrinkly

Teeth: Turn yellow

Mouth: Persistent bad breath

Throat: Becomes dry and raw, increased risk of throat cancer (Throat cancer can damage your voice box, which will affect your ability to speak, drink, eat, and even breathe.)

Lungs: Blacken, air sacs die, breathing becomes difficult (Smoking makes your lungs weaker and unable to fight off infections. People who have smoked for a long time are at risk for lung cancer, chronic bronchitis, or emphysema.)

Heart: Blood vessels narrow, beats faster (If your arteries and other blood vessels get narrower, your heart has to work extra hard to pump blood through them. This puts added strain on your heart.)

Bones and Joints: Impairs formation of new bone

Skin: Becomes dry and wrinkly (Smokers look older than nonsmokers and often appear pale and unhealthy.)

(Note: In addition you may want to point out that the lingering smell of smoke leaves clothes, hair, and even furniture smelling unpleasant and stale.)

- Distribute *Drug Awareness*, pencils, and crayons to each student. Review the directions and tell the students how much time they have to complete the activity.
- Have each student show the class one drawing on his/her completed activity sheet.

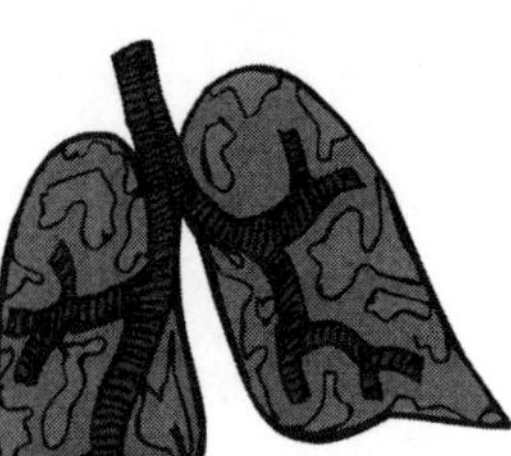

DRUG AWARENESS

Smoking hurts many parts of your body.

Directions: Circle the body parts that smoking affects. Under the body parts you have circled, draw a picture of what you think that body part will look like after years of smoking.

LUNGS	TEETH	SKIN
FINGERS	**HEART**	**EYES**
MOUTH & THROAT	**NOSE**	**BONES & JOINTS**

DRUG AWARENESS LESSON PLAN II

GRADES 2-5

Materials Needed:

- ☐ Copy of *Drug-Free Trash Can Basketball Questions* (page 199) for the leader
- ☐ Trash can
- ☐ Any ball (kickball, basketball, tennis ball, etc.)
- ☐ Chalkboard and chalk or dry erase board and marker
- ☐ Piece of tape

Pre-Presentation Preparation:

Place a trash can in the front of the classroom.

Draw a team scoreboard on the board.

Decide where the student who is shooting the basket should stand. Place a piece of tape on the spot on the floor where the student is to stand.

Presentation:

- Divide the students into two teams.

- Ask for a volunteer from one team to be the catcher and stand behind the trash can. Explain that the ball cannot be caught *above* the trash can, but only behind it or on its sides.

- Ask for a volunteer from the other team to keep score at the board.

- Tell the students:

  Each team will send one student to the front of the room at a time. I will ask that person a question. If the student answers the question correctly, he or she will get a point and get the chance to earn a bonus point by making the basket. (Note: Try to give lots of clues to any student who does not know the answer. The purpose of this lesson is to teach and review the concepts. It is not intended to be a major competition between the two teams.)

- Have one student from the first team come to the front of the room. Ask the student a question. If the question is answered correctly, the scorekeeper gives the team a point. Then the student stands at the tape on the floor and attempts to throw the ball and make a basket. If the student makes a basket, the scorekeeper gives the team another point.

- Continue the game until everyone has had a turn. Remember at the end to give both the catcher and the scorekeeper a turn.

- The team that earns the most points is the winner.

DRUG-FREE TRASH CAN BASKETBALL QUESTIONS

1. What are the names of three different drugs?
2. What is the drug in cigarettes that is so addicting?
3. What do cigarettes do to your body?
4. What does *addicted* mean?
5. How old do you have to be to legally drink alcohol?
6. How old do you have to be to legally smoke cigarettes?
7. What is *marijuana*?
8. How is marijuana bad for you?
9. Is it legal to smoke marijuana at any age?
10. What does alcohol do to your body?
11. Why do people say not to drink alcohol and drive?
12. What should you do if you see your friend trying a cigarette?
13. What should you do if your babysitter drinks alcohol when he/she is babysitting you?
14. Who are the only people who should give you medicine?
15. Should you take medicine by yourself?
16. Can smoking kill you? How?
17. Why does smoking make it difficult to breathe?
18. What disease can smoking cause?
19. Why are cigars just as bad as cigarettes?
20. Is beer safer than wine?
21. What can happen to you if you are caught with drugs?
22. TRICK QUESTION! How old do you have to be to legally smoke marijuana?
23. Why do we celebrate National Red Ribbon Week each year?
24. Can you play sports if you take drugs? Why or why not?
25. If you have questions about drugs, whom can you ask?

DRUG AWARENESS STUDENT EVALUATION

NAME ________________________________ **DATE** ____________

TEACHER ________________________________

Please answer the following questions about the Drug Awareness lessons **HONESTLY**:

1. I enjoyed the counselor coming to the classroom. (Please circle one.)

   A LOT **A LITTLE** **NOT AT ALL**

2. I learned things in this class that I didn't already know. (Please circle one.)

   A LOT **A LITTLE** **NOT AT ALL**

3. The thing I liked best about this class was:

   ____

   ____

4. The thing I didn't like about this class was:

   ____

   ____

5. Three (3) things I learned in this class were:

   A. ____

   ____

   B. ____

   ____

   C. ____

   ____

RED RIBBON ACTIVITIES

Dear Parents:

We are celebrating Red Ribbon Month. I will be visiting classrooms and discussing the importance of being drug free. We are also having a poster contest, complete with prizes. The students may design these posters at school or at home and the whole family may help. We are planning a special week when the students will wear things that promote being drug-free. These days are as follows:

Monday—Give Drugs The Slip (wear bedroom slippers)
Tuesday—Drugs And I Don't Mix (wear mismatched clothes)
Wednesday—Team Up Against Drugs (wear something displaying your favorite team)
Thursday—I'm Proud To Be Drug-Free (wear all red)
Friday—Living Drug-Free Is No Sweat (wear sweat shirts and sweat pants)

When I visit the classrooms, I will be talking about heroes. I will be discussing how heroes are kind, fair, honest, respectful, responsible, dependable, and drug-free. I will discuss how heroes can be parents, grandparents, firefighters, police officers, teachers, or whoever is there when you need help and who makes life better for you. I will explain that a hero is someone the children would be proud to be like when they grow up.

Our big activity this year will be a HERO PARADE on ____________________________. Each student will make his/her hero at home by stuffing clothes with newspaper, making a face out of tights or nylon hose, dressing the hero up, and adding a sign or nametag. These heroes will be in the Hero Parade and then be placed in our Hero Hall Of Fame for all to see. Prizes for participation will be awarded.

Our goal, of course, is to make each child aware of the positive impact people who choose to be drug-free can have on one another.

Please talk with your children about the dangers of drugs, including alcohol and tobacco products, and discuss the importance of Red Ribbon Month. Many books and materials in the local library can help children understand the importance of being drug-free. If you have any questions, please do not hesitate to contact me at (_____)________________ .

Thank you,

____

RED RIBBON ALERT!

Dear Parents:

Red Ribbon Month is here once again. We have planned many activities to celebrate the children's choice to be free of tobacco, alcohol, and other drugs. I will be visiting all of the classrooms and passing out a red bracelet to each child. Each child will design a poster to put in the window of his/her parent's car. These posters will tell others to be drug-free. The children will make these posters in the classroom with me.

Each class will choose a 1st, 2nd, and 3rd place winner. Each winner will receive a prize. The 1st place winners will play *Shoot Hoops For Red Ribbon.* These students will have a basketball contest against some of the teachers. However, the teachers will have to throw the ball farther. The winners will get donuts for breakfast the next morning at school.

We will wear special things during Red Ribbon Week. Students may receive prizes for wearing the designated color or item, but they will not know what day that may happen. For example, all 4th-graders wearing crazy hats may receive pencils.

These are the special days:

Monday—Drug-Free Roundup (wear your favorite jeans)
Tuesday—Sock It To Drugs (wear your weirdest socks!)
Wednesday—Hats Off To Being Drug-Free (wear a crazy hat)
Thursday—I'm Too Bright For Drugs (wear sunglasses)
Friday—Taking Drugs Is Backwards (wear clothing backwards)

If you have any questions about the Red Ribbon festivities, please do not hesitate to contact me at:

(__________)________________________________.

Thank you,

____

Dear Parents:

As you know, drug awareness is a vital component of the ___ -grade curriculum. Students are inundated with the anti-drug message from Red Ribbon Week in October to the DARE graduation ceremony in May. This message can never be overstated.

I would like to reinforce our commitment to this anti-drug message by sponsoring an evening "Lock-In" for all _____ -graders. "Locked-In" On Refusing Drugs will be held on ____________. Beginning at _____ p.m., the students will be involved in many anti-drug activities and projects. Pick-up time will be at _____ a.m., but you will be invited to see your child perform a skit at _____ p.m. To attend the "Lock-In," each child will be required to complete a community service and write a summary of his/her efforts. The project will be due no later than ______________. Suggestions for these projects are enclosed. The packet contains a list of objectives I hope to reach, a detailed schedule of activities, requirements for participation, and a list of things students will need to bring that evening. In addition, you will find a permission slip and a volunteer sign-up form.

Obviously, I will not be able to accomplish all of this without adult volunteers. If you can participate, please sign and return the volunteer sign-up form by ____________________ .

I will solicit donations of supplies and materials from local businesses. If you know of anyone who would be interested in donating something from the enclosed list, please let me know.

I know this can be an exciting and memorable event for our _____ -graders. The lessons will last a lifetime.

Sincerely,

DATES TO REMEMBER:

_________________ Student's Permission Form Due

_________________ Adult Volunteer Form Due

_________________ Community Service Project Deadline

_________________ "Locked-In" On Refusing Drugs*

* This event is a special night for ____ -graders and parents only. Please leave siblings at home.

GRADERS ARE "LOCKED-IN" ON REFUSING DRUGS

OBJECTIVES

To learn the importance of refusing drugs, including alcohol and tobacco

To recognize the importance of community service

To practice cooperation and team-building skills

VOLUNTEERS AND SUPPLIES NEEDED

1. **ACTIVITY: SETUP AND CLEANUP**
   Setup date: ______ **Cleanup date:** ______
   Volunteers needed: Decorations, setup and cleanup
   Supplies and materials needed: Crepe paper and balloons (red and white), banners from counselor, tables and chairs for the activities, drug-free music, activity signs

2. **ACTIVITY: REGISTRATION AND T-SHIRT MAKING**
   Volunteers needed: 1 adult to sign students in and 1 adult to obtain parent's signatures and emergency forms, 5 adults to help students write names on their T-shirts and decorate them
   Supplies and materials needed: 1 large expandable file with alphabet, sign-in and sign-out sheet, copies of emergency forms, 10 permanent markers, 10 pens, 5 bottles of each color of fabric paint (example: 5 red, 5 blue, etc.), lots of newspapers for drying freshly painted T-shirts

3. **ACTIVITY: COMMUNITY MEETING**
   Volunteers needed: Police officer, substance abuse coordinator
   Supplies and materials needed: Copies of schedule, activities and their locations, and rules

4. **ACTIVITY: K-9 UNIT DEMONSTRATION**

5. **ACTIVITY: RESTROOM BREAK**
   Volunteers needed: 2 male restroom monitors, 2 female restroom monitors

6. **ACTIVITY: MOTIVATIONAL SPEAKER**

7. **ACTIVITY: RESTROOM, SNACK, AND RAFFLE DRAWINGS**
   Volunteers needed: 3 people to pass out pizza, cookies, napkins, paper plates, paper cups, and punch and to help the students clean up; 2 male restroom monitors, 2 female restroom monitors
   Supplies and materials needed: Pizza, cookies, napkins, paper plates and cups, punch

8. **ACTIVITY: SWAT TEAM**
   Volunteers needed: 2 adults to monitor children when they look in the SWAT truck

over➡

9. **ACTIVITY: PRACTICE SKILLS AND RESTROOM**
Volunteers needed: 10 adults to help students break into groups and write and practice skits about refusal skills, 2 male restroom monitors, 2 female restroom monitors
Supplies and materials needed: 10 legal pads, 20 pens or pencils, props such as schoolbooks, balls, etc.

10. **ACTIVITY: PERFORM SKITS FOR PARENTS**

11. **ACTIVITY: SIGN OUT AND GO HOME**
Volunteers needed: 2 adults to make sure each child's parent signs his/her child out
Supplies and materials needed: Sign-in/sign-out paper, pens

Just Say No

☐ **I can volunteer for:**

☐ **I can provide some of the following needed supplies and materials:**

My name ______________________________

My child's name ______________________________

My child's homeroom teacher ______________________________

My home telephone number (__________**)** ______________________________

My work telephone number (__________**)** ______________________________

Please return this form to ______________________ **by** __________.

"LOCKED-IN" ON REFUSING DRUGS SCHEDULE

	Registration
	Community Meeting
	Guest Speaker
	Activity Explanations
	Activity Locations
	Rules For Behavior
	K-9 Unit
	Restroom Break
	Motivational Speaker
	Pizza, Cookies, Restroom Break
	SWAT Team
	Practice Skits And Restroom Break
	Perform Skits For Parents
	Go Home

FRIDAY NIGHT

7:00-7:30	Registration
7:30-8:00	Community Meeting
	Theme Song
	Guest Speaker
	Activity Explanations
	Activity Locations
	Rules For Behavior
8:00-8:15	Restroom Break
8:15-10:40	Activity Center Rotation
10:40-11:00	Restroom Break And Snack
11:00-11:30	Group Talent Show
11:30-12:00	Drug-Awareness Movie
12:00	Lights Out

SATURDAY MORNING

7:00-7:45	Breakfast And Cleanup
7:45	Parent Pickup

ACTS OF COMMUNITY SERVICE REQUIRED TO ATTEND "LOCK-IN"

The students are required to choose one of the following items and complete a project summary:

- Neighborhood: One hour of non-profit service will be required. This could be babysitting, shoveling snow for the elderly, cleaning up a cul-de-sac, etc.
- Recycling Project: Collect plastic bags to return to the grocery store, make useful things out of things you would normally throw away, etc.
- Visit a nursing home and take flowers, pictures, etc. to someone you *do not* know.
- School Pride Project: School-wide clean-up, reading stories to younger students before and after school (for this, the student will be responsible for coordinating and implementing these activities on his/her own time).
- Collecting items for Goodwill, etc.

If the project is not approved by the student's homeroom teacher, it may not be accepted.

Each student will be required to write a summary of his/her project and his/her parents must sign it. The summary must include the following:

1. Main idea with 5 details to support it
2. A minimum of 10 sentences
3. New information learned by doing the project
4. Answers to WHY, WHAT, WHERE, HOW, WHEN questions about the project
5. Parent's signature
6. Signature of homeroom teacher

STUDENT "LOCK-IN" PERMISSION FORM

CHILD'S LAST NAME ____________________

CHILD'S FIRST NAME ____________________ M.I. ____

ADDRESS ____________________

CITY ____________________

STATE __________ ZIP CODE __________

____

PARENT'S NAME ____________________

HOME PHONE # ____________________

WORK PHONE # ____________________

CELL PHONE # ____________________

MOTHER ____________________

FATHER ____________________

CHILD'S NAME ____________________

☐ WILL
☐ WILL NOT

attend the "Lock-In" on ______________________ . I understand all of the requirements and expectations included in this packet and give my permission for my child to attend and participate in all of these activities.

In addition, I understand I will immediately pick up my child during the "Lock-In" if any adult thinks it is necessary due to illness, behavior, attitude, or unforeseen circumstances.

Just Say No

____
PARENT'S SIGNATURE

Please return this form and the volunteer and supplies-needed form by ______________ .

NOTE: Each student will need to bring a plain white T-shirt for decorating

Dear ________________________________,

Thank you so much for volunteering for the "Lock-In." I could not have done it without you. I bet you have never been so tired!

The students seemed to really enjoy the evening and, most importantly, they seemed to learn a great deal about the dangers of alcohol and other drugs.

Your time and dedication to our school, for this event and others, is a statement to the children about how important it is to parents and other community members that they grow up to be successful citizens.

Again, thank you very much for your time and dedication. You are what made the "Lock-In" successful and a memorable experience for all who attended.

Sincerely,

Dear Everyone at ________________________________:

Thank you so much for donating ________________________ for raffle prizes to the "Locked-In" On Refusing Drugs program. The students loved receiving them.

Programs such as this cannot be successful without many people pulling together their time, energy, money, and resources. It could not have happened without community members like you.

We truly could not do these things for our students without your help and your dedication to our children. Thank you again for supporting our schools.

Sincerely,

PROFESSIONAL RESOURCES

ADDITIONAL RESOURCES—COUNSELOR FORMS—RESOURCE CENTER | PARENT HANDOUT

The Parent Resource Center in the guidance office has the following materials for you to borrow. This lending library is available to all parents in our school and is open from ________ to ________ on ______________. Each resource may be kept for two weeks. You will find helpful books, videos, and DVD's on a variety of subjects. The materials available now are:

...se take advantage of this opportunity to enhance you... ...nting skills.

...truly,

244
COUNSELORS' PAGES © 2006 MAR•CO PRODUCTS, INC. 1-800-448-2197

PROFESSIONAL RESOURCES—STAFF SUPPORT | STUDENT TEACHER WELCOME LETTER

The checklist on the back of this sheet must be completed daily.

When each item is completed and checked, the list must be turned in to me at the end of each day. This list should help you remember essential daily activities.

The items on this list are essential for any primary teacher. Hopefully, this will be an easy way for you to practice and keep track of each skill. I will place these forms in your file to share with your university advisor so she/he can see that we are working on each of these skills.

Good luck! I am so glad you are with me in my classroom.

REMINDER:

Computer and Internet work should be done only at the following times:

✓Before students arrive
✓During rest time
✓During planning time
✓After children leave

220
COUNSELORS' PAGES © 2006 MAR•CO PRODUCTS, INC. 1-800-448-2197

PROFESSIONAL RESOURCES—COUNSELOR FORMS—COUNSELOR EVALUATION | ADMINISTRATOR

COUNSELOR'S REVIEW

COUNSELOR:

SCHOOL(S):

DATE:

ADMINISTRATOR COMPLETING EVALUATION:

Counseling Responsibilities

1. **Direct Services to Students (Small Group/Individual):** Provides guidance to help students deal with behavior management, friendship issues, self-esteem, social skills, grief, organizational skills, anger management, handling bullies, separation anxiety, divorce, impulsivity, etc.
   ☐ SATISFACTORY ☐ IMPROVEMENT NEEDED
2. **Direct Services to Staff (Consultative Services):** Helps teachers work with students experiencing behavior problems, social/emotional problems, a lack of organizational skills, a lack of motivation, school anxiety, a lack of homework skills, low self-confidence, alleged abuse, etc.
   ☐ SATISFACTORY ☐ IMPROVEMENT NEEDED
3. **Direct Services to Parents (Parent Conferences, etc.):** Assists parents with home/school behavior-management plans, helps them cope with their child's social/emotional needs, helps them motivate their child to succeed academically, etc.
   ☐ SATISFACTORY ☐ IMPROVEMENT NEEDED
4. **Indirect Services (Communication Regarding Guidance Programs and Procedures:** In the beginning of each school year, each child takes home a packet that contains a guidance permission form, a detailed list of guidance services/procedures, and special guidance programs and activities that are planned throughout the year. In addition, letters are sent home before each special program to remind parents and invite them to participate.
   ☐ SATISFACTORY ☐ IMPROVEMENT NEEDED
5. **Comments Regarding General Rapport With Staff, Parents, and Students:**
   ☐ SATISFACTORY ☐ IMPROVEMENT NEEDED
6. **Additional Comments:**
7. **Overall Evaluation Rating**
   ☐ SATISFACTORY ☐ IMPROVEMENT NEEDED

EVALUATOR'S SIGNATURE ______________________ DATE __________

COUNSELOR'S SIGNATURE ______________________ DATE __________

236
COUNSELORS' PAGES © 2006 MAR•CO PRODUCTS, INC. 1-800-448-2197

STAFF SUPPORT

S.M.I.L.E. PROGRAM (pages 217-219) **SW TH**
(Support and Motivation In A Learning Environment)

This program is designed to help teachers and instructional assistants who may be having a difficult time with a child's behavior. Teachers and instructional assistants volunteer to be on the S.M.I.L.E. committee by signing up on the calendar outside of the counselor's office. Once a week the committee meets for 30 minutes with a teacher or instructional assistant who is requesting help with a behavioral issue in his/her classroom. The group brainstorms to try to help the teacher develop useful strategies. Below are some forms you may use with this program.

S.M.I.L.E. Program (page 217) **SW TH**

This sheet explaining the S.M.I.L.E. program should be reproduced and given to all teachers and instructional assistants.

S.M.I.L.E. Form (page 218) **SW TH**

Teachers or instructional assistants use this form to request help from the S.M.I.L.E. committee.

S.M.I.L.E. Meeting Reminder (page 219) **SW TH**

This is a reminder slip for an upcoming S.M.I.L.E. meeting. Complete the reminder by printing the name of the teacher or instructional assistant on the first blank and the date and time on the second blank.

Student Teacher Welcome Letter (page 220) **SW TH**

This form introduces a student teacher and welcomes him/her to the classroom.

Student Teacher Checklists (pages 221-222) **SW TH**

These checklists can help a student teacher remember essential responsibilities. It can also help a cooperating teacher keep track of how well the student teacher is performing and areas in which he/she can improve. The checklist on page 221 may be used as is or as a guideline. The checklist form on page 222 may be modified to your own personal expectations.

S.M.I.L.E. PROGRAM

(**S**upport And **M**otivation **I**n A **L**earning **E**nvironment)

WHAT AND WHY?

The S.M.I.L.E. program is designed to allow counselors to brainstorm with teachers who may be having a difficult time with a child's behavior in the classroom. Three experienced teachers and I will sit down with the teacher and try to develop a plan of action to help control the child's behavior in the classroom. This informal meeting will leave you with specific strategies you can try in your classroom the very next day.

WHAT IT IS NOT!

This is not a long process of forms and follow-up meetings.

HOW?

You will find a plastic file box outside of the Counseling Office. Use the calendar in the file box to sign up on the day most convenient for you. Complete the *short* form (name, problem, etc.) and place the completed form in the file.

THEN WHAT?

Decide whether you want suggestions, a plan of action, behavior charts complete with stickers and rewards, or an in-depth plan that involves calling the parents in for a conference, etc. After our meeting, you may sign up for a follow-up meeting if you would like to discuss your successes or if you need more suggestions. Or you never have to meet with us again.

Please let me know if you have any questions.

S.M.I.L.E. FORM

(**S**upport And **M**otivation **I**n A **L**earning **E**nvironment)

STEP 2:

Teacher's Name

Child's Name

Today's Date

What behavior would you like to change?

Briefly, what have you tried so far?

Don't forget to sign up on the calendar (STEP 1) and place this completed form in the folder (STEP 3) outside my office. We will help you any way we can. Thank you.

Meeting Reminder

______________________________,

We have a S.M.I.L.E. meeting in my office at

______________________________.

SEE YOU THERE!

The checklist on the back of this sheet must be completed daily.

When each item is completed and checked, the list must be turned in to me at the end of each day. This list should help you remember essential daily activities.

The items on this list are essential for any primary teacher. Hopefully, this will be an easy way for you to practice and keep track of each skill. I will place these forms in your file to share with your university advisor so she/he can see that we are working on each of these skills.

Good luck! I am so glad you are with me in my classroom.

REMINDER:

Computer and Internet work should be done only at the following times:

✓ Before students arrive
✓ During rest time
✓ During planning time
✓ After children leave

STUDENT TEACHER CHECKLIST

WEEK OF ____________

	MON	TUES	WED	THURS	FRI
BEFORE SCHOOL					
Greet each child by name	☐	☐	☐	☐	☐
Guide children to various activities	☐	☐	☐	☐	☐
Sit in the center of room while students complete before-school activities	☐	☐	☐	☐	☐
When the morning bell rings, remind the children to clean up and guide them to their seats	☐	☐	☐	☐	☐
Ask children for notes, money, folders, library books, etc.	☐	☐	☐	☐	☐
Conduct opening exercises	☐	☐	☐	☐	☐
DURING SCHOOL					
After giving directions each time, ask children to repeat	☐	☐	☐	☐	☐
Complete daily goal sheets—don't forget early dismissals (Check with me before sending sheets home)	☐	☐	☐	☐	☐
DURING RECESS AND PLAY TIME					
Work individually with a child on a skill that needs improving	☐	☐	☐	☐	☐
and/or					
Monitor children on the computers	☐	☐	☐	☐	☐
and/or					
Closely watch children's interpersonal relationships by being in close proximity to them	☐	☐	☐	☐	☐
DISMISSAL TIME					
Remind children to take boots, hats, lunchboxes, etc.	☐	☐	☐	☐	☐
Stand by the door and make sure children are zipped and ready to go	☐	☐	☐	☐	☐
AFTER SCHOOL					
Clean up from day's activities	☐	☐	☐	☐	☐
Prepare materials for next day	☐	☐	☐	☐	☐
Update/erase board for next day	☐	☐	☐	☐	☐

STUDENT TEACHER CHECKLIST

WEEK OF ____________

	MON	TUES	WED	THURS	FRI
BEFORE SCHOOL					
DURING SCHOOL					
DURING RECESS AND PLAY TIME					
DISMISSAL TIME					
AFTER SCHOOL					

COUNSELOR FORMS

Counselors need many forms.
They use forms for parents, administrators, children, and outside agencies.

THIS SECTION INCLUDES:

Reproducible Needs Assessment Form
Reproducible Intern Permission Form
Reproducible Evaluation Forms
Reproducible Record-Keeping Forms
Reproducible Suspected Child-Abuse Form

Needs Assessment (page 227) **TH**

In order to effectively meet the needs of an individual school, counselors cannot rely on only their own judgment. The opinions of the people they service—teachers—are necessary. Reproducing this form and distributing it to each teacher will help you to make your program more efficient.

Yearly Program Review (page 228) **CR**

This form provides an immediate record of the programs conducted by the counselor for the year. Record the topic and grade levels for each classroom program and small-group counseling program presented each month. Decide whether to include names of the students participating in the groups. For individual counseling and parent contacts, write either the total number of contacts made for the month or record the names of the students and parents seen.

Student Observation Form (page 229) **CR**

Counselors are often asked to do classroom observations on students. This form provides an easy-to-use format for quickly recording the data observed.

Notification of Consultation (page 230) **TH**

Reproduce this form and distribute it to teachers who have referred a student for a Child Study Team or similar format appraisal.

Let's Meet (page 231) **TH**

An effective way to communicate with teachers is to set aside one or two days twice during the school year to meet and discuss the class as a whole. The first meeting should be at the beginning of the year. At that time you can share pertinent information about students that you feel would be helpful in making the student's year productive. The second meeting should be in the latter part of the year to obtain input from the teacher as to how the class has progressed and any concerns about placement for the upcoming year.

What's New (page 232) **TH**

This form is designed for those counselors who provide materials for teachers to use in their classrooms. Make a list of the materials available and distribute the form to each teacher.

Intern Permission Form (page 233) **PH**

Confidentiality is a major component of counseling. This form is to let parents know someone may be observing their child during counseling sessions. The parents then have a choice of whether or not they want the intern in the office when the counselor is in session with their child.

Referrals (page 234) **CR**

This form tells the counselor and the administration the number of student referral requests and can be tallied by the month or for several months.

Counselor Evaluation Forms (pages 235-236) **AH**

Administrators use these two forms when evaluating the counselor.

Staff Evaluation Forms (pages 237-238) **TH**

This form may be reproduced and given to staff. Having staff evaluate the counseling program will give the counselor an accurate picture of how the counseling program is being viewed by the entire staff and valuable information about future services.

Student Survey (page 239) **SH**

Student feedback is as important as adult feedback. A simple form given to students in a classroom can immediately tell the counselor if his/her goals for student interaction are being met. Use this form once each year near the end of the term.

Parent Guidance Survey (page 240) **PH**

This form that may be reproduced and given to parents will provide the counselor with information about the effectiveness of parental contacts.

Standardized Testing Letter (page 241) **PH**

Reproduce this letter for every parent who has a child in a grade that will be tested. Fill in the testing dates and send the letter home a week before the testing will begin.

Teacher Conference Report (pages 242) **CR**

Have this form handy whenever you are involved in a teacher conference. Use it as a guide as to what should be accomplished during the conference. After the conference is concluded, immediately complete the form for your files.

Parent Conference Report (pages 243) **CR**

The *Parent Conference Report* is a quick overview of the conference. It should be completed during the parent conference and signed by all attending personnel. Reproduce a completed copy and give it to each attending party.

Parent Resource Center (page 244) **PH**

This form is designed for those counselors who provide a parent resource library. Add the available materials to the letter and send it home to parents.

Telephone Call Record (page 245) **CR**

Reproduce these forms for more efficient record-keeping. Counselors receive many telephone calls and this form, kept near the telephone, may be completed and filed immediately after completing the call.

Report Form For Suspected Child Abuse (page 246) **CR**

All suspected child-abuse cases must be reported. This form gives the counselor the opportunity to record the incident and pass the report on to the required authorities.

NEEDS ASSESSMENT

As a member of our staff, it is my desire to learn about things you feel need to be addressed by the guidance program. Your concerns are important and will be taken seriously. Please take a few moments to complete the following. Thank you in advance for your cooperation.

Name ____________________ Grade ______

Thinking about our student body, what guidance-related concerns do you see our students facing? ____________________

What would be some beneficial approaches to address these concerns? ____________________

It is important that guidance and teachers work together. In addition to what is already being done, what other ways can the guidance department help you in your job? ____________________

Classroom guidance is an important function of the guidance counselor. What classroom guidance topics would be a priority for your class? ____________________

Small-group counseling is a way to key in on specific concerns for particular students. What small-group topics do you feel need to be addressed? ____________________

The guidance department works closely with parents. What suggestions do you have for programs or services for parents?

____

The guidance department works closely with the pupil personnel support staff. What suggestions do you have for improving this service? ____________________

Please add any additional comments or suggestions that you feel were not covered above. ____________________

YEARLY PROGRAM REVIEW

Year ______ School ______ Counselor ______

MONTH	INDIVIDUAL CONTACTS	SMALL-GROUP COUNSELING	CLASSROOM PROGRAMS	PARENT CONTACTS
August				
September				
October				
November				
December				
January				
February				
March				
April				
May				
June				

STUDENT OBSERVATION FORM

Student's Name ____________________ Grade ________

Teacher ____________________

Class Observed ____________________

Date of Observation ________ Time Spent on Observation ________

Reason for Observation:

Observation Notes:

Conclusions:

Follow-up Procedure:

Counselor's Signature ____________________ Date ________

NOTIFICATION OF CONSULTATION

TO ____________________ **DATE** __________

A time has been set aside to review the progress and needs of:

____

Date __________

Time __________

Place __________

WE CARE ABOUT KIDS

The following people will be in attendance:

____

____

During this time, we will discuss:

____

____

____

- -

If you have any other issues which need to be addressed, please list them below.

____

____

____

If this meeting has been scheduled during class instruction time, someone will be sent to cover your class. Please have instructions for them to follow.

☐ I will be in attendance at the meeting for ____________________ on ________.

☐ I am not able to make the meeting for ____________________.
Please reschedule the meeting.

Teacher's signature ____________________

After completing this form, please return the lower section to ____________________ *by* __________

TEACHER'S NAME ____________________ **GRADE** ________

It's time for our beginning of the year meeting to discuss your class and any concerns you have about the students or the class as a whole. In order for me to have any necessary information on hand, please list the names of any students you would like to discuss.

The meeting is scheduled for ______________________. Someone will arrive to monitor your class while we are meeting. Please have work assigned for your students or an activity for the monitor to do during this period.

LET'S MEET

TEACHER'S NAME ____________________ **GRADE** ________

It's time for our end of the year meeting to discuss your class and any concerns you have about the students or the class as a whole. In order for me to have any necessary information on hand, please list the names of any students you would like to discuss.

The meeting is scheduled for ______________________. Someone will arrive to monitor your class while we are meeting. Please have work assigned for your students or an activity for the monitor to do during this period.

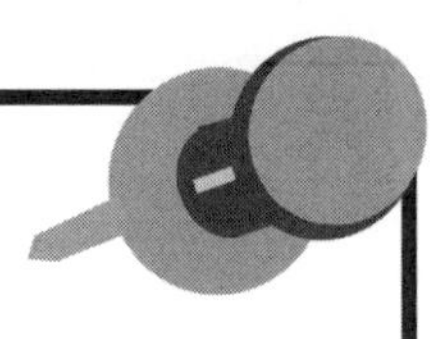

Some new materials are available for you to check out for your classroom. They are:

These materials are in the guidance resource area and can be obtained by filling out the check-out card in the box. If what you want is not available, please fill out a reserve card. When it comes back, you will be notified.

Dear Parents:

I am fortunate to have a college student from ______________________________ interning with me for a period of time during this school year. __________________ wants to be an elementary school counselor and is very interested in what the job entails.

I take confidentiality very seriously when speaking with children in my office. If you give your permission for this student to sit in on my individual and/or group counseling with your child, please sign below.

Please let me know if you feel uncomfortable with this. If so, I will assign other things for my intern to do during my sessions with your child. If you have any further questions, please do not hesitate to contact me.

Sincerely,

____

WE CARE ABOUT KIDS

Intern Permission Form

☐ **YES.** I give permission for my child, ___________________________, to speak with the counselor while the intern from ____________________ is present.

☐ **NO.** I would prefer that the counselor see my child with no other adult present.

______________________________________ PARENT'S SIGNATURE

__________ DATE

REFERRALS

COUNSELOR ______________________________

SCHOOL ______________________________

MONTH ____________________ YEAR __________

STUDENT'S NAME	REFERRED BY	DATE SEEN
1. ____________	____________	________
2. ____________	____________	________
3. ____________	____________	________
4. ____________	____________	________
5. ____________	____________	________
6. ____________	____________	________
7. ____________	____________	________
8. ____________	____________	________
9. ____________	____________	________
10. ____________	____________	________
11. ____________	____________	________
12. ____________	____________	________
13. ____________	____________	________
14. ____________	____________	________
15. ____________	____________	________

NOTES:

COUNSELOR EVALUATION FORM

DATE:

COUNSELOR:

SCHOOL(S):

ADMINISTRATOR COMPLETING EVALUATION:

Overall Performance Assessment

S Satisfactory/Acceptable Performance
I Improvement Needed
N/A Not Applicable

COUNSELING TECHNIQUES AND SKILLS			
Individual Counseling Services	**S**	**I**	**N/A**
Small-Group Counseling Services	**S**	**I**	**N/A**
Parent Conference Services	**S**	**I**	**N/A**
Classroom Guidance Services	**S**	**I**	**N/A**
Career-Education Activities	**S**	**I**	**N/A**
Drug Awareness Activities	**S**	**I**	**N/A**
Community Contacts/Referrals	**S**	**I**	**N/A**
Professionalism	**S**	**I**	**N/A**
School Involvement	**S**	**I**	**N/A**
Personal Characteristics	**S**	**I**	**N/A**

ADDITIONAL COMMENTS

EVALUATOR'S SIGNATURE ______________________ DATE ____________

COUNSELOR'S SIGNATURE ______________________ DATE ____________

COUNSELOR'S REVIEW

DATE:

COUNSELOR:

SCHOOL(S) :

ADMINISTRATOR COMPLETING EVALUATION:

Counseling Responsibilities

1. **Direct Services to Students** (Small Group/Individual):
Provides guidance to help students deal with behavior management, friendship issues, self-esteem, social skills, grief, organizational skills, anger management, handling bullies, separation anxiety, divorce, impulsivity, etc.

☐ SATISFACTORY ☐ IMPROVEMENT NEEDED

2. **Direct Services to Staff** (Consultative Services):
Helps teachers work with students experiencing behavior problems, social/emotional problems, a lack of organizational skills, a lack of motivation, school anxiety, a lack of homework skills, low self-confidence, alleged abuse, etc.

☐ SATISFACTORY ☐ IMPROVEMENT NEEDED

3. **Direct Services to Parents** (Parent Conferences, etc.):
Assists parents with home/school behavior-management plans, helps them cope with their child's social/emotional needs, helps them motivate their child to succeed academically, etc.

☐ SATISFACTORY ☐ IMPROVEMENT NEEDED

4. **Indirect Services** (Communication Regarding Guidance Programs and Procedures):
In the beginning of each school year, each child takes home a packet that contains a guidance permission form, a detailed list of guidance services/procedures, and special guidance programs and activities that are planned throughout the year. In addition, letters are sent home before each special program to remind parents and invite them to participate.

☐ SATISFACTORY ☐ IMPROVEMENT NEEDED

5. **General Rapport With Staff, Parents, and Students:**

☐ SATISFACTORY ☐ IMPROVEMENT NEEDED

6. **Additional Comments:**

7. **Overall Evaluation Rating:**

☐ SATISFACTORY ☐ IMPROVEMENT NEEDED

EVALUATOR'S SIGNATURE ______________________ DATE ____________

COUNSELOR'S SIGNATURE ______________________ DATE ____________

STAFF EVALUATION

STUDENT REFERRAL

1. Have you ever referred a student to the school counselor?
   ☐ YES ☐ NO

2. If so, approximately how many times have you made a referral during this school year?
   ☐ 1-3 ☐ 4-6 ☐ 7 or more

3. Approximately how many referrals, in all, have you made in the last three years?
   ☐ 1-3 ☐ 4-6 ☐ 7 or more

COUNSELOR CONSULTATION

4. Have you ever discussed a student problem with the counselor?
   ☐ YES ☐ NO

5. If so, approximately how many times have you discussed student problems with the counselor during this school year?
   ☐ 1-3 ☐ 4-6 ☐ 7 or more

6. Approximately how many times have you consulted with the counselor regarding a student in the last three years?
   ☐ 1-3 ☐ 4-6 ☐ 7 or more

QUALITY OF SERVICES

7. Immediacy: When you contacted the counselor, how immediate was the response? If fair or poor is checked, please explain.
   ☐ Excellent ☐ Good ☐ Fair ☐ Poor

8. Did the counselor follow-up with you periodically? If fair or poor is checked, please explain.
   ☐ Excellent ☐ Good ☐ Fair ☐ Poor

9. Effectiveness of Guidance Services: Did the contact with the counselor produce positive results such as positive behavior changes, a positive change in attitude, or a student's better understanding of a difficult topic or situation? If fair or poor is checked, please explain.
   ☐ Excellent ☐ Good ☐ Fair ☐ Poor

10. Was the counselor available for conferences with you and/or parents at a time that was convenient for you? If fair or poor is checked, please explain.
    ☐ Excellent ☐ Good ☐ Fair ☐ Poor

GUIDANCE SERVICES

COUNSELING SERVICES

1. What prompted you to use the guidance services? Please check as many as apply.

   ☐ Academic issues
   ☐ Behavioral issues

   Issues related to:

   ☐ Death
   ☐ Divorce
   ☐ Family changes
   ☐ Friendship
   ☐ Self-esteem
   ☐ Separation anxiety
   ☐ Other ______________________.

2. What counseling services do you use for your students most frequently?

   ☐ Individual counseling
   ☐ Small-group counseling
   ☐ Consultation regarding a student

3. What do you think is the most helpful aspect of the elementary guidance services at this school?

4. What changes would you make to the elementary guidance program at this school?

CLASSROOM GUIDANCE

1. How often do you think the guidance counselor should go into the classrooms for a 25-30 minute lesson?

   ☐ Weekly
   ☐ Bi-monthly
   ☐ Monthly
   ☐ Only if teacher requested
   ☐ Not at all
   ☐ Other ______________________.

2. What topics would you like the counselor to cover during classroom guidance lessons?

   ☐ Friendship
   ☐ Self-esteem
   ☐ Feelings
   ☐ Conflict resolution
   ☐ Responsibility
   ☐ Behavior
   ☐ Problem-solving
   ☐ Social skills
   ☐ Inappropriate language
   ☐ Peer pressure
   ☐ Study skills
   ☐ Self-control
   ☐ Manners
   ☐ Work habits
   ☐ Careers
   ☐ Goal-setting
   ☐ Drugs
   ☐ Good choices

I teach ______ grade (optional) at ______________________________ Elementary School.

STUDENT SURVEY

1. Did you know there is a counselor in your school?
   ☐ YES ☐ NO

2. What is your school counselor's name? ______________________________

3. Why do you think your school has a counselor?

   ____

   ____

   ____

4. Has the counselor visited your classroom?
   ☐ YES ☐ NO

5. Do you know where the school counselor's office is located?
   ☐ YES ☐ NO

6. Have you ever visited the school counselor's office?
   ☐ YES ☐ NO

7. What have you learned from your school counselor?

   ____

   ____

   ____

8. What would you like to learn from your school counselor?

   ____

   ____

   ____

PARENT GUIDANCE SURVEY

1. Are you aware guidance services are offered in your child's school?
   - ☐ Yes
   - ☐ No

2. If yes, approximately how many times have you used these services in the last three school years?
   - ☐ 0
   - ☐ 1-3
   - ☐ 4-6
   - ☐ 7 or more

   If you have used the school guidance services, please complete the next five questions. If not, please proceed to question #6.

3. Communication: Did the counselor return your phone calls promptly and update you with your child's progress? If fair or poor is checked, please explain.
   - ☐ Excellent
   - ☐ Good
   - ☐ Fair
   - ☐ Poor

4. Effectiveness of Guidance Services: Did your contact with the counselor produce positive results such as a positive behavior change, a positive change in attitude, or a better understanding of a difficult topic or situation? If fair or poor is checked, please explain.
   - ☐ Excellent
   - ☐ Good
   - ☐ Fair
   - ☐ Poor

5. What concerns encouraged you to use the guidance services? Please check as many as apply.
   - ☐ Academic changes
   - ☐ Behavioral changes
   - ☐ Death of family member
   - ☐ Death of pet
   - ☐ Divorce
   - ☐ Family change
   - ☐ Friendship issues
   - ☐ Self-esteem issues
   - ☐ Separation
   - ☐ Other ____________________

6. What changes would you make to the elementary guidance program at this school?

7. What do you think is the most helpful aspect of the guidance services at your child's school?

8. Should classroom guidance take place:
   - ☐ Weekly
   - ☐ Bi-monthly
   - ☐ Monthly
   - ☐ Only if teacher requested
   - ☐ Not essential
   - ☐ Other____________________

9. What topics would you like the guidance counselor to cover in the classroom?

☐ Friendship	☐ Bullying
☐ Study skills	☐ Self-esteem
☐ Drugs/Alcohol	☐ Peer pressure
☐ Stereotyping	☐ Racism
☐ Diversity	☐ Family changes
☐ Responsibility	☐ Cooperation
☐ Careers	☐ Respect
☐ Conflict resolution	☐ Assertiveness
☐ Kindness	☐ Foul language
☐ Lying	☐ Cheating
☐ Fairness	☐ Gangs
☐ Weapons	

My child(ren) attends:

____________________ Elementary School

My child(ren) is (are) in:

______, ______, ______, grade(s).

Dear Parents:

The time of year has come for standardized testing. Your child will be tested on the following dates:

Please write these dates on your calendar so you can help us prepare your child to do the best job he/she can do. Below are some suggestions for preparing your child for testing:

1. Make sure your child has plenty of sleep the night before testing.

2. Let your child choose in advance his/her favorite breakfast. Make sure it consists of some form of protein and carbohydrates for energy.

3. Explain that the purpose of the test is just to show the teachers what information the child already knows. Explain to the child that he/she will not know every answer and that is okay.

4. Remind your child to take his/her time and do the very best possible job he/she can.

5. Set up a special reward or privilege your child can look forward to at home for doing his/her best on each day of testing.

If you have any questions, please do not hesitate to call me at (_______)_________________.

Sincerely,

____

YOUR CHILD'S COUNSELOR

TEACHER CONFERENCE REPORT

STUDENT'S NAME

PHONE

SCHOOL

TEACHER GRADE

APPOINTMENT DATE TIME

CONFERENCE REQUESTED BY

PERSONS IN ATTENDANCE:

____

____

1. CONCERN (S): ______________________________

____

____

____

2. ACTION AGREED UPON:

TEACHER ______________________________

____

____

____

COUNSELOR ______________________________

____

____

____

3. FOLLOW-UP CONFERENCE: ☐ YES ☐ NO

IF YES, WHEN AND WHERE? ______________________________

TEACHER'S SIGNATURE ______________________________

COUNSELOR'S SIGNATURE ______________________________

PARENT CONFERENCE REPORT

STUDENT'S NAME

GRADE

TEACHER

PARENT IN ATTENDANCE

DATE

CONFERENCE REQUESTED BY

REASON FOR CONFERENCE:

NOTES:

FOLLOW-UP TO BE DONE:

By The Teacher

By The Counselor

By The Parent

Next Parent Meeting Date

Time

Counselor's Signature ____________________

The Parent Resource Center in the guidance office has the following materials for you to borrow. This lending library is available to all parents in our school and is open from ______ to ______ on ________________. Each resource may be kept for two weeks. You will find helpful books, videos, and DVD's on a variety of subjects. The materials available now are:

Please take advantage of this opportunity to enhance your parenting skills.

Yours truly,

TELEPHONE CALL RECORD

COUNSELOR ______________________________

PERSON MAKING CALL ______________________________

DATE ____________________ TIME ____________________ AM/PM

MESSAGE:

FOLLOW-UP CALL NEEDED: ☐ YES ☐ NO

TELEPHONE CALL RECORD

COUNSELOR ______________________________

PERSON MAKING CALL ______________________________

DATE ____________________ TIME ____________________ AM/PM

MESSAGE:

FOLLOW-UP CALL NEEDED: ☐ YES ☐ NO

REPORT FORM FOR SUSPECTED CHILD ABUSE

(Copies forwarded to the building principal, the director of Special Pupil Services, and the director of Human Resources at the local police department.)

TODAY'S DATE ____________

CHILD'S NAME ____________ BIRTH DATE ____________
ADDRESS ____________
CITY ____________ STATE ________ ZIP CODE ____________
COUNTY ____________

FATHER'S NAME ____________
ADDRESS ____________
CITY ____________ STATE ________ ZIP CODE ____________
COUNTY ____________

MOTHER'S NAME ____________
ADDRESS ____________
CITY ____________ STATE ________ ZIP CODE ____________
COUNTY ____________

INTAKE WORKER'S NAME ____________
CASEWORKER'S NAME (IF CURRENTLY AVAILABLE) ____________
CASE NUMBER ____________
REPORTED BY ____________
SCHOOL ____________
PHONE NUMBER ____________

DESCRIPTION OF INCIDENT/INJURY

REBECCA C. SCHMIDT

Rebecca C. Schmidt earned her undergraduate degree from the University of Texas at San Antonio. She received her master's degree in counseling from Tarleton State University in Stephenville, Texas. She taught elementary school for four years and has been an elementary school counselor for 13 years. She is currently a counselor in the Mayfield City School District in Mayfield Heights, Ohio.

Rebecca resides in Mayfield Heights with her husband, Craig, and their daughters, Hannah and Lauren.

Dedication

This book is dedicated to our two precious little girls, Hannah and Lauren. May their lives be filled with wonderful health and happiness.

INSTRUCTIONS FOR USING THE CD

The CD found on the inside back cover provides two types of files:

ADOBE® PDF FILES:

System requirements to open PDF (.pdf) files:
Adobe Reader® 5.0 or newer (compatible with Windows 2000® or newer or Mac OS 9.0® or newer).

These files offer the user color versions of the reproducible pages found in the book. The pdf files are sorted into folders that correspond to the sections found in the book. For example: The *01_IndBehaviorpdf* folder contains pdf files of the reproducible pages found in *Section 1/Individual Behavior*. The number in the file name refers to the page number in the book. For example: *page14_counpages.pdf* is the same as page 14 in the book.

These files cannot be modified/edited.

MICROSOFT WORD® FILES:

System requirements to open Microsoft Word® document (.doc) files:
Microsoft Word® 98 for Mac and 2000 for Windows® or newer (compatible with Windows 2000® or newer or Mac OS 9.0® or newer). To avoid font substitution, you will need the following fonts installed: Times, Wingdings.

In order to modify these files, you will need a basic knowledge of how to use Microsoft Word. Prior to using these files, you will need to make a copy of the .doc files. The CD is read-only. This prevents the user from permanently losing the original file format. The Microsoft Word document files are sorted into folders that correspond to the sections found in the book. For example: The *03_GetStarteddoc* folder contains document files of some of the pages found in *Section 3/Getting Started*. The number in the file name refers to the page number in the book. For example: *page19_counpage.doc* is the text from page 19 in the book.

These text-only files were provided for those counselors who wish to design their own forms and letters, but do not want to re-type the entire page. Not every page is included as a document file. The CD includes only forms/letters that may need modification to suit your individual needs. After adapting a Microsoft Word document, you may give the form/letter your own personal touch by adding your own clipart, modifying the fonts and color, then printing it on school letterhead or color/specialty paper.